March 2014

Styla —

Please accept this book as a gift —

I hope you enjoy reading it — much of the material is dealing with "stuff" we deal with all the time.

Our friendship and relationship both professional + personal is a wonderful part of my life —

Carl

A Timely Scenario

BY GILBERT MARTIN M.D.

ILLUSTRATED BY DAVE ARKLE

ISBN: 1494875195
ISBN-13: 9781494875190

To my family, who has been a part of many of these scenarios.

Table of Contents

Perspective:
A Timely Scenario

This book is a collection of essays and editorials published in the *Journal of Perinatology* from 1984 to 2000. I produced these pieces as "fillers" to be interspersed with scientific articles. These "Timely Scenarios" were written under the pseudonym "The Perinate." They were intended to be satirical, predictive, humorous, timely and it is interesting how years later many of these concepts have become reality. Some of the names that appear in these essays are real; most others are reconstructed. All of the scenarios I describe, however, are totally fictitious.

I am reproducing this material because I am now sitting on a different perch. The thoughts of a young, proactive, "wanting to immediately alter the status quo neonatologist" have changed... mellowed. My forty-plus years in neonatology have been an adventure as we have progressed from decisions based on anecdotal experiences to decisions derived from evidence-based medicine.

Read these essays with a second cup of coffee, before turning out the light, or perhaps when a chuckle or two might brighten your day.

I need to acknowledge my assistant, Sandy Skelley, who has been with me "forever"; Dave Arkle, who provided the illustrations for these pieces; my wife Pat, who was the "wordsmith goddess"; and Nature Publishing for allowing me to reproduce these "Timely Scenarios."

I hope you enjoy reading these essays as much as I enjoyed writing them.

Gilbert I. Martin, MD (aka The Perinate)

FOREWARD
Avory A. Fanaroff, M.D.

Gil Martin served as the editor of the *Journal of Perinatology* for many years. He did this with great passion and as a labor of love. As with all his projects, he infused his energy into the journal and through his editorials and other written contributions was able to project his enthusiasm and intellect, which added character and personality to the emerging fields of neonatal and perinatal medicine.

In order to avoid "white space"—in other words blank pages and half pages—he let his imagination and writing skills roam free as he presented contemporary problems in the form of essays, dialogues, monologues, and even poems. He originally published these pieces under the nom de plume "The Perinate." Gil Martin has now assembled these writings into this beautifully illustrated coffee table book, *A Timely Scenario.* Remarkably, for some of the scenarios, time has stood still, and they could be referred to as "Timeless Scenarios." For example, in spring 1986, he depicts large government deficits with significant budget cuts and crunch time for the health-care industry, leading to significant reductions in the workforce. This was accompanied by rising fetal and neonatal mortality rates. In addition research funding decreased. Fast forward to 2013, and a similar scenario exists. Most troublesome is the reduction in research funding, because research drives the advances that translate into better clinical outcomes. It is sad but true that we have to continue to fight for every research dollar for child health programs; after all, children are the future of our nation.

As noted in Gil Martin's "Perspective," the pieces were meant to be "satirical, predictive, humorous, and timely." They certainly are, and the characters remind me of those of Damon Runyon, an American newspaperman and author whose subjects invoked a distinctive social type. Medicine in general and neonatal and perinatal medicine have undergone a sea change in the past thirty years since these essays were first conceived. Evidence-based medicine has replaced anecdotal medicine, and the rapid discoveries related to the human genome indicate that individualized or personal medicine is just around the corner. *A Timely Scenario* is a lighthearted but very effective and enjoyable way of looking back and learning about the evolving history of neonatal and perinatal medicine. The anecdotes highlight social and economic issues, as well as the emerging advances in clinical care. Medicolegal problems are also highlighted.

I congratulate Gil Martin on assembling *A Timely Scenario*. The book is a valuable contribution to the history of the "infancy" of neonatal and perinatal medicine and is a collection that Damon Runyon would have said is "more than somewhat" worth reading.

"Imagination is the living power and prime agent
of all human perception."
Samuel Taylor Coleridge

PREFACE
Alan R. Spitzer, M.D.

Formalized as a branch of pediatrics during the 1970s, the subspecialty of neonatal-perinatal medicine has but a relatively recent past in the great tradition of medicine. Perhaps the singular event that led to the recognition of the neonate as a unique patient was the premature birth of Patrick Bouvier Kennedy to President and Mrs. Kennedy in 1963, several months prior to President John F. Kennedy's assassination. Today, that infant, who weighed 2.1 kilograms (4 lbs 10 oz), would present almost no serious problems to the experienced neonatal intensive-care team, and completely intact survival would be expected. In that era, however, Patrick Kennedy's treatment was profoundly rudimentary, and he expired within two days. The attention brought by his tragic death, however, created an awareness in the country that the newborn infant deserved a far more sophisticated level of care than was available at that time and resulted in the initial creation of neonatal intensive-care units (NICUs) around the country.

While the concept of neonatal intensive care was greeted almost universally with enthusiasm and high energy, the reality was that the NICU was the modern-day medical analogy of the Wild Wild West. The critically ill neonate, in a very real sense, represented completely uncharted territory for those who dared to breach its borders. Basic principles of newborn physiology were poorly understood; the types of problems and diseases that were being diagnosed and treated had never been seen before; and initially the available tools (IVs, ventilators, medications, etc.) often required makeshift adaptations from adult medicine that were less than satisfactory. Great ingenuity and creativity were therefore critical essentials for any physician who dared venture into this new field of practice that seemingly did not obey the usual rules. While each new day in the NICU was energizing and exciting, finding a successful pathway through the maze of uncertainty was always challenging. Fortunately a key group of leaders in the field of neonatology soon emerged, and few people were more instrumental in paving the way through this new subspecialty than Gil Martin.

As a clinical neonatologist, teacher, collaborator, writer, editor, and thought leader, Gil has contributed to the creation of the subspecialty of neonatology—one of the great success stories in modern medicine—in ways that cannot be overstated. He has influenced the careers of many people while simultaneously saving the lives of many infants. Fortunately for all of us, while giving so much of himself to make life better for others, Gil immediately recognized the commonality of experience that many of us in this new field shared. He understood the need to document some of the history of the evolution of newborn medicine. But in his own marvelous style, Gil also recorded his observations with a spirited twinkle in his eye and a great sense of bemusement of the struggle that was the creation of neonatal medicine, especially in its early years.

Preface

In this book you will find Gil's collection of many of his best pieces of writing—ones that show how the world of the NICU and the neonate looked during those formative times. Anyone who has practiced inside the intensive-care nursery immediately will smile and recall similar babies, families, circumstances, and experiences, both frustrating and rewarding, that caregivers encounter on a daily basis. While I read this book, an avalanche of memories came back to me, many of which I hadn't thought about for sometime, often accompanied by a good laugh and a sense of wonder at how rapidly and positively the world has changed for the tiny babies under our care. But that is the talent of a great storyteller—the ability to evoke strong feelings and emotions with simple words and observations, and there is no better storyteller (or NICU poet) than Gil Martin.

It has been my privilege to know Gil now for many years, and he truly has lived the life of a great and caring physician-teacher. He has taken the time to let us really see what that life has been all about, and the vignettes and poems he offers in this book are timeless and universal. Though he wrote many of these pieces twenty to thirty years ago, their lessons remain as vivid and as meaningful as the day he penned them.

Take a seat, and put everything aside for a few moments in your busy day. Be prepared to learn a lot, gain some new insights into the world of the neonate, and be wonderfully entertained at the same time. This book is simply great reading, and by the time you put it down, you will be a far more perceptive individual and a much better clinician.

Reduce the Fat...Not the Substance
(Spring 1984)

Her clothes were well worn yet neatly pressed. Her shoes, an often-neglected object of the poor or rushed, were not stylish, but polished and clean. A trifle too much makeup could not disguise dreary eyes and a well-lined brow. Even a few minutes of idle chatter did not soften or remove the tension above her eyes. She was painfully thin, and her large abdomen exaggerated her spindliness.

"I've been trying to come in for nine weeks," she said. "No appointments, no doctors, no nurses, no money, they keep telling me." She continued, "with two babies at home, I can't work. At first the food stamps helped, but now they hardly ever come. Whatever

I get feeds the kids, and lately I'm just too tired—just tired. You know what I mean? I'm yelling at everyone."

She continued nonstop, in short sentences, with hurried breaths. I let her go on until the nurse knocked on the window and pointed to her watch.

"Can I ask you something?" I interrupted.

"Wha…?" she said, stuttering.

"What have you eaten today, let's say for breakfast and lunch?"

"I had a cup of coffee for breakfast, and beans and a cracker for lunch, with a can of soda," she answered.

"What will you eat for dinner?" I asked.

She didn't look at me right away. Her eyes focused somewhere beyond me. "I don't know," she whispered.

"Why don't you follow the nurse so I can examine you," I continued, rising from my chair, ill at ease.

Moments later my clinical suspicions were confirmed. She had gained only twelve pounds during thirty-six weeks of pregnancy, and she was hypertensive and malnourished. "There are several tests we have to do," I said, instructing the nurse to order an ultrasound, a nonstress test, and an estriol. "Try to do these as an emergency," I told her.

The nurse nodded and said as she left the room, "emergency, emergency…all the doctors say, 'emergency.' "

"Can I get dressed now?" the woman asked.

I nodded and said, "try as best as you can to eat as much as possible these next few weeks, especially nutritious foods. I want to see you again next week." She was gone without another word. Relieved that she had left, I felt drained, but I couldn't forget her look.

I never saw her again but learned later that she delivered a 1650 gram small-for-gestational-age infant who remained in the neonatal intensive-care unit for one month but appeared to have a good prognosis.

The irony is that due to budget cuts and rollbacks, fewer women are receiving adequate prenatal care today. The mortality rates for infants is slowly rising in a number of states, as maternal care clinics have turned away patients due to decreasing funds and varying eligibility requirements. What the government does not realize is that it costs $30 to $50 per month to provide nutritional supplements to a pregnant woman while neonatal intensive care drains thousands of dollars per patient.

Reducing funding for needed perinatal programs may indeed improve the federal deficit theoretically. In actuality, the amount of money spent for health care will increase, eliminating the benefits of the restrictions. Preventive perinatal medicine is the key to improved mortality and morbidity statistics. Reduce the fat...Not the substance.

Submitted by Perinate
Apples or Cookies?

It is lunchtime at a parochial school in New York and the students are lined up to pick up their lunch. At the front of the table, there is a big bowl of apples and the nuns had written in front of the bowl, "only take one, God is watching". On the other side of the table is a big bowl filled with chocolate chip cookies. One of the students had written, "take as many as you want, God is watching the apples".

With the Affordable Care Act and Obamacare, will Healthcare Providers be offered the apples or the cookies? Perhaps...... neither.

DRG Outlier
(Summer 1984)

My first admission of the day seemed simple enough, a 1600 gram male infant, born to a twenty-eight-year-old woman, gravida 4, after inadequate prenatal care. The infant's Apgar score was 5 and 7 at 1 and 5 minutes, respectively, and grunting was noticed immediately. Clinical and x-ray findings were consistent with respiratory distress syndrome. The infant was three hours old and was receiving 43% oxygen, with adequate blood gases. The problem was not with the clinical management of the patient. The new hospital admitting forms were specific concerning the key issues of the patient's DRG (Diagnosis-Related Group), and I knew primary and secondary diagnoses would have to be continually updated. I asked the nursery secretary for the DRG manual and learned that the maximum length of stay allowed for a 1600 gram infant with RDS, according to the present "weight factors" and considering the "geometric mean for Los Angeles County," was 18 days, 7 hours, and 42 minutes. Scanning the DRG charts, I noticed that if the baby had weighted 1500 grams, I would have been able to get another seven days of hospitalization.

The financial office was called and made aware of the infant's condition, and it was explained that they had better get their staff ready for immediate action if complications occurred or further hospitalization was necessary.

During rounds the next day, the infant was stable, with no real improvement. Dr. Flent, the attending physician, skipped over the clinical data and asked, "Have you sent the patient's information to the grouper?" A medical student rotating on our service had not heard this term before, and we explained that "the grouper" was the name for the computer that would take the whole record, sift through all possible diagnostic categories, and come up with the diagnosis that would offer the best payment and the longest allowance for hospital stay .

"Have you taken into account the weight factor?" Dr Flent continued.

"At 1600 grams, we have an excellent chance of saving this infant, barring any major complications," I said.

"No, no," said Flent. "I'm talking about the weight factor we consider in allowing for continual hospitalization. What do they teach you these days in your training?"

The weight factor tells us what amount the government will pay, what the hospital case mix has been, and what the area fee for such a service provides. The conversation never returned to a discussion of the medical plan for the infant, and I must admit feeling a bit disillusioned.

During the next few days, the baby's condition improved, but he did not tolerate oral feeding.

"Send for the nutritional outlier," said Flent.

The nutritional outlier's sole responsibility was to devise ways to extend the hospital stay on the basis of a change in the infant's nutritional problems. During the next several days, we also needed the services of the surgical outlier and the apnea and bradycardia outlier. Rounds soon consisted of the nursery attending physician, a neonatal fellow, two members of the house staff, the nursing coordinator, the neonatal social worker, the grouper technician, the financial advisor to the nursery, and three to five outliers, depending upon the status of the infant.

HEARING SCREEN OUTLIER
NUTRITIONAL OUTLIER
SURGICAL OUTLIER
OPTHALMOLOGY OUTLIER
APNEA & BRADYCARDIA OUTLIER
GENETIC OUTLIER
INFECTIOUS DISEASE OUTLIER

Reams of paper describing the new DRGs and the coding and recoding of the outliers appeared on the chart. Despite all these nonclinical problems, the infant's condition improved, and finally he was ready for discharge.

During the discharge-planning conference, I reviewed with both parents the infant's problems in the hospital and what would be necessary for follow-up in the future. The mother then remarked that two of her children at home had chickenpox and that the heater was broken. She asked if we could we keep the baby one more day until she could make arrangements to board the children and fix the furnace. My immediate reaction was favorable, but my answer was immediately stopped by the apnea and bradycardia outlier, who informed me that we would need another outlier to permit the extra day of hospitalization.

"Handle it," I yelled, not caring about tone or demeanor. I wanted something done because it was right, and the decision shouldn't be bound by cold rules and regulations.

"I'm sorry, Doctor," was the reply. "There is no outlier for compassion. The baby will have to leave the hospital and find another place."

The idea struck suddenly. I picked up the phone and dialed. "Honey," I asked, "how would you like to be an outlier for a day?"

Double-Blind Study
(Fall 1984)

Our nursery rounds began that day with a brand-new team,
who could know that I would shortly raise my voice and scream?
From my cords a low-pitched wail increased to finally bellow,
as I addressed the intern, two residents, and fellow.
"Examination, proper lab work, and no excessive frills,
will improve mortality and sharpen up your skills."
The two residents' demeanors were just like night and day,
awaiting pearls of wisdom, I wondered what they'd say.
John was more aggressive as he discussed the PDA,
"Indocin not surgery, it seems the only way."
Lynn pointed out clotting problems, and decreased urine flow,
"double-blind with follow-up, that's how we'll finally know."
"Do we now use tocopherol to save the preemie eye?"
said John, discussing oxidants, and how they work and why.
"The IV prep," said Lynn, "caused increased mortality,
double-blind with follow-up—the only truth to me."
"Agree that intralipid in parenteral nutrition,
gives the needed calories and is above suspicion."
"Not so," said Lynn, "There are potential hazards with this med,
double-blind with follow-up, and then I'll go to bed."

A Timely Scenario

Phenobarb in IVH, discussed the residents,
provided a lively repartee; it finally made some sense.
One would push for therapies untested, or so new,
the other needed evidence, with larger numbers too.
Rounds became a battlefield around the nurses' station,
postulates and therapies, with proof of complication.
I hoped each would soften some, retaining love and caring,
John could moderate his thoughts, Lynn could add some daring.

Compromise was not accomplished in the month we shared,
I wondered how Administration allowed them to be paired.
As they left I wished them luck in their future missions,
I'd wait to hear the bellowing…of the obstetricians.

Submitted by Perinate
DRGs for Perinatology

Perinatologists and neonatologists are trying to understand the complexity of new healthcare models. These include Accountable Care Organizations (ACOs) and Pay for Performance (P4P) initiatives. In addition, reimbursement strategies such as Medicaid, Partial Private Pay and Diagnostic Related Groups (DRGs) will further complicate the process.

I can see in the future a "DRG Relocation Center" where like trades in baseball and football, patients will be transferred from one hospital to another based upon open beds, types of patients and number of days available per DRG diagnoses. Like the stock market there will be a "DRG Pit" where large consoles, NASA-looking electronic displays will detail hospitals depicted in different colored lights. Trading two intensive care babies for one critical baby will become the norm as professional traders work the floor.

A new cottage industry is born.

Baby Doe
(Winter 1984)

The "Baby Doe Law" is the name of an amendment to the Child Abuse Law passed in 1984 in the United States that sets forth specific criteria and guidelines for the treatment of seriously ill and/or disabled newborns, regardless of the wishes of the parents.

The violin legato of the third movement was interrupted by a shrill beeping——; this sound continues to produce a momentary flutter and diaphoresis, even though I've carried the beeper for years.

After calling my service, I was instructed and placed a second call immediately.

Two rings later a voice answered. "This is Doctor 464, the TL of the DHHSSABDS." The voice, somewhat harsh, was authoritative.

"What? Who is this, and what do those letters mean?" I asked.

The voice continued, "I am the team leader of the Department of Health and Human Services' Special Assignment Baby Doe Squad. The Federal Government requests that you meet with other team members tomorrow morning at the United Airlines counter at Kennedy Airport in New York. Your plane ticket is waiting for you. Bring enough clothing for three days, and tell your family that you are on special assignment for the United States Government. Are there any questions?"

Several hours later, after confirming that there was indeed such a special-assignment squad, my curiosity forced me to seek three days of coverage, appease my family, and change my schedule.

A Timely Scenario

After catching the night flight from Los Angeles to New York, I arrived in time and was met by a formal-looking gentleman who silently assisted me with my luggage and escorted me to a waiting limousine. The rear compartments of the limousine were comfortable enough, but I must admit I felt some distress, as the darkened window did not enable me to estimate how fast we were going.

After arriving at our destination, my baggage was taken, and I was ushered into a conference room, where several others stood around chatting.

"Welcome aboard, Doctor," said a thin, wiry-looking man who approached me. One of his hands was outstretched and held a nametag. "We don't use names here," he said. "For the remainder of your stay, you'll be number 637. Please sit down." Doctor 464, the team leader, explained that the Department of Health and Human Services had requested that all of us meet to decide whether a particular hospital had discriminated against a handicapped infant and utilized improper care. We would have full access to the chart, family, nursing, and the medical and paramedical personnel. Copies of the *BDCISOPM* (*Baby Doe Complaint Investigation Standard Operating Procedures Manual*) were handed out, and we were instructed to familiarize ourselves with the material.

Baby Doe

For the next three days, the committee sat for twelve to fourteen hours a day, interviewing the parents and other family members. We reviewed the chart extensively, and the unfortunate infant was examined. The nursery supervisor, chief resident, pediatric staff, and neonatologists spent the entire period with the committee. At various times, the group questioned staff nurses, staff members, social workers, and paramedical personnel, who expressed their views and opinions.

Because of the great burden placed upon the nursery personnel, two transfers from outside institutions were refused, and three patients needed to be transferred to other facilities due to lack of support personnel.

The house staff bitterly complained that the neonatologist and chief resident were not available for rounds, and it was felt that the standard of care in the nursery deteriorated during this period of time.

To me, the discussion of the particular handicapped infant seemed less important than the total upheaval the committee had caused within the hospital setting. Each evening we were escorted to a hotel, and like a sequestered jury, we were carefully denied access to all media materials, so as not to be prejudicial in our judgment.

On our fourth day, the committee decided that the care offered the infant was totally appropriate. However, in addition we felt that the destructive effects on the hospital were inappropriate and that the care offered to the remaining infants in the neonatal intensive-care unit was substandard during this period. In addition the cost to the government for the committee's expenses, the emotional trauma placed upon the parents, family, and medical staff, and the fiscal loss to the hospital were not reasonable.

A simple incident, spawning controversy, had now lost perspective, and relying upon harsh investigation had proceeded to supersede medical judgment and human compassion.

Clinician versus Researcher
(Spring 1985)

I had heard rumors that Dr. Elmer Frankel was getting tired of doing primary laboratory perinatal research, so I wasn't surprised when the phone rang late Thursday afternoon.

"Bob, it's El Frankel. How are you?"

"Fine, fine," I answered. "I haven't seen you for ages. How are things in the lab?"

"That's why I'm calling. I've been working on hormones, tissues, and nonclinical issues for seven years now in the basement of the research building. I don't even have a window. I know I've lost my clinical touch. Bob, listen to me," he said in an almost whining tone, "I need to get back to the nursery. Can you swing it?"

"Elmer, seven years is a long time. There have been so many changes. Things are…just…so different. Do you think—?"

"Wait, wait, go no further," he stuttered out quickly. "I've kept up, read the journals, gone to meetings. I'm ready, believe me."

"El, I'm not speaking of clinical variations, but more of administration, fiscal policies, and personnel changes. It's not like the old days when you and I were residents. Do you remember when we used to make morning rounds in the nursery? We'd walk through the door, and a kind of hush would fall over the whole room. The nurses in crisp white gowns would stand up and not only answer questions and assist, but also cater to our every wish. The secretaries, therapists, and all of the other personnel would wait around for orders. It seemed so organized, so easy. We never worried about staffing, didn't need government permission for every action and reaction. Damn it, we felt that we were really taking care of patients!"

"Hold on a sec Bob," Elmer said. "Things couldn't have changed that much. I'm sure you're the same guy, taking care of patients in the same way. Listen—give me a tour of the nursery this afternoon. I haven't been out of the basement for weeks."

"Fine, fine," I answered, sort of caught up in the previous moment's outburst. "Come up around two o'clock. I'll show you around. My office is in room 601B. See you then."

Knowing this might be an important meeting, Elmer had chosen his outfit carefully: gray slacks, a striped blue shirt, a solid blue tie, penny loafers, and a starched white lab coat.

"Let's see," he murmured to himself. "Stethoscope in the right pocket, six tongue blades, two pens, and a flashlight in my breast pocket. I guess I'm set."

As the elevator door opened to the sixth floor, Elmer inhaled the clean antiseptic linoleum smell. *Ah, just like old times*, he thought. Walking down the hall, he noticed with interest the titles on the passing doors. The largest office had a blazoned sign that read, Clinical Neonatal Nurse—Department Head. As he walked down the hall, the office doors seemed smaller but the titles more intriguing: Clinical Neonatal Nurse Supervisor, Neonatal Nurse Clinician, Neonatal Clinical Coordinator, Head Neonatal Nurse, Neonatal Unit Manager, Neonatal Research Coordinator, Neonatal Medication Nurse, Neonatal Team Leader, Neonatal Charge Nurse, Neonatal Discharge Planning Nurse, Neonatal Nursing Instructor for Continuing Outreach Education.

The doors, as in the *Alice in Wonderland* tale, grew smaller as the titles increased in size. Room 601B was the last door at the end of the hall. The title on the door read, Sr. Neon. The letters were small, frayed, and not impressive. Elmer hesitated for a moment. Suddenly a voice from inside called, "El, is that you? Come in! Come in!"

The room was a peanut shell. Books, papers, and diet-soda cans were strewn about. Everest-like mounds of articles were cluttered on, around, and about every surface.

"It's small and messy, but I know where everything is," I said, smiling.

Elmer looked at me and didn't say anything at first.

"Bob, don't you wear a shirt and tie anymore? When did you grow the beard?"

I looked at my Adidas tank shirt and my New Balance running shoes and smiled.

"Things are just…more relaxed in nurseries today—less formal, no real codes of conduct or dress, for that matter. You know, *laidback*. Come on. I'll introduce you to Faye, one of the nurses."

"Which nurse is she?" Elmer asked. "I noticed the different titles."

"Oh, Faye is the Neonatal Unit Manager. She's in charge of schedules and vacations—a very important lady to have on your side, believe me. She knows all about staffing. And that's the name of the game today."

We walked down the hall to one of the larger offices. The clatter of typewriters welcomed us as we walked into the room.

"Toni," I said, "is Faye in? I want to introduce El…I mean, Dr. Frankel, to her."

"Oh. Hi, Bob," said Toni, turning quickly. "I'll ring her office."

"She calls you Bob?" whispered Elmer, eyes wide open.

"Shh, hold on a minute," I said.

Toni turned away, dialed a number, murmured something into the phone, turned, and said, "She's putting the finishing touches on tonight's schedule. It should take 10-15 minutes more. Can you wait?"

"No, I think not," I said. "Tell her to plan for triplets." I winked. "I'll look for Denise or Maggie instead." Elmer was breathing down my neck as I walked out of the office.

"She calls you Bob?" he asked again. "I've never heard of such a thing."

Before I could even answer him, three other nurses passed us in the hallway and, in chorus, said, "Hi, Bob. What's going on?"

We entered the door labeled NEONATAL INTENSIVE-CARE UNIT, removed our rings and watches, scrubbed for the required three minutes, and put on pink-and-blue hospital gowns.

"No masks or headgear?" Elmer asked.

"It's not cost effective," I answered, "and there's been no proof that wearing anything else decreases the infection rate."

The sounds of "I Write the Songs" blared from a speaker some-where in the nursery as we walked in.

"Is that Manilow or Diamond?" I asked Elmer.

"Wha...what did you say?" His mouth was open, but I could only hear a gurgle.

I walked over to the stereo receiver and turned off the music. Elmer followed closely, as if afraid to separate from me.

"Bob, no one has even looked up," Elmer said. "Do they know we're here?"

"Watch this," I told him. "Hellllooooo, girls!" I shouted, cup-ping my hands over my mouth like a horn. Denise, team leader for the afternoon shift, looked up from her charting and said tersely, "Bob, we're women, not girls. After all we don't call you *boys*."

"Denise, this is Dr. Frankel. He may be working with us soon in the nursery. Who are you taking care of today?"

"This is baby Stone, a growing preemie—just about to go home."

"When is the baby going to be discharged?" asked Elmer, in a deep, resonant, professional tone. "What medication is the baby taking?"

"Let's see…" She hesitated. "Vitamins for sure, but the Medication Nurse can supply you with all the exact details. The Neonatal Nutrition Nurse has all the calories counted and can tell you about the formula. Should I call her?" Without waiting for an answer, Denise turned and walked away. Elmer looked bewildered.

"Bob, if all these specialized nurses take care of separate parts of the baby's care, then what does Denise do?"

"I'm not sure," I answered. "That's the responsibility of the nursing administration. But although things are different, *the system works*. At least I think it does."

"It's not for me," said Elmer. "I'd rather hear Mozart and catheterize fetal lambs."

I smiled as we walked out of the nursery and sang softly, "I write the songs that make the young men cry. I write the songs… I write the songs…"

Newborn Protection
(Summer 1985)

Karol's unexpected telephone call interrupted a rather busy, unproductive, paper-shuffling day. "Drew," she began, "I've got great news. The promotion came through. It's just what I want."

"Great, great, honey," I replied. Karol had been trying to land this job as chief x-ray technician for two years, and it seemed that all her hard work had now paid off.

"Let's celebrate." Karol continued. "Make reservations at Villa Rosa's at eight o'clock. I'll meet you there."

"OK, honey. I'll see you then." I hung up feeling a special glow. Karol was seven months pregnant, feeling well, and able to continue working. She also had received great progress reports from her obstetrician, Dr. Copeland. I decided to call the restaurant and ask them to place a bottle of Brüt Champagne on the middle of the table, surrounded by a dozen yellow roses.

I arrived at Villa Rosa's at the same time as Karol, kissed her quickly, and ushered her inside. She looked stunning in a black-silk maternity dress that didn't make her appear too heavy. She wore just the right amount of makeup, with a touch of Giorgio perfume. I looked at her, smiled, and thought how lucky I was to have married this wonderful woman. We sat down, and I immediately asked the waiter to pour the Champagne. We toasted to Karol's new job and decided to order.

"What would you like this evening, madame?" the waiter asked.

"I think I'll have breaded veal cutlet, pasta Alfredo, and a baked potato. Please bring black coffee with dinner."

"Would you care for any other vegetables?" the waiter continued.

"I think not," replied Karol.

"And for you, sir?" he said, turning toward me.

"I'll have the antipasto and veal scaloppini with a side order of eggplant, and bring me a Lite beer as well.

"Very good, sir," he said, as he turned and walked away. I poured another glass of Champagne, and Karol and I talked for a few moments. Suddenly the maître d' appeared in front of us.

"*Buonasera*," he began.

"Good evening," I replied.

"I am sorry to interrupt your dinner, but Mr. Skurow, the manager of the restaurant, would like to see you both in his office. It's important. Please follow me."

"What about our dinner?" I exclaimed.

"Dinner will wait for your return," he replied. "Please follow me."

Rather bewildered, quite annoyed, and hungry, Karol and I followed him into the manager's office. Mr. Skurow was fiftyish and rather suave, with graying hair and jet-black eyes that darted quickly as he spoke.

"Please sit down," he said, as he motioned us to a small couch at one end of the room. He sat down at a desk at least ten feet from us across a plush British-racing-green carpet.

Hoping to quickly take the offensive, I said, "I hope you have an adequate explanation for interrupting our dinner."

"Yes, yes, yes," he continued. "As you know, Mr.…eh…?"

"Rubin," I replied.

"Ah, yes, Mr. Rubin, the Protect the Newborn Act, which Congress passed in 1988, is quite specific about do's and don'ts regarding pregnant women, in an attempt to protect the unborn child from illness and stress. All restaurants, employers, physicians, and industries have had to read and understand the law and abide by it. You know about the law, don't you? Your obstetrician should have been quite explicit about it."

Newborn Protection

"Dr. Copeland did mention the law," I said, "but he is old fashioned about his practice and actually didn't spend too much time telling us about it. What, if anything, does this have to do with interrupting our dinner and spoiling a perfectly good evening? Please get to he point, and be brief. We're both hungry, and my wife, who's seven months pregnant, in case you haven't noticed, needs her nourishment."

"Yes, yes, yes," he continued. "The law specifically states that pregnant women shall *not* be allowed to consume alcoholic beverages of any type during pregnancy, and they are also not allowed to use caffeine products of any sort. There have apparently been some problem cases in the courts stating that a baby was injured by the mother having even an occasional drink and a few cups of coffee during pregnancy. The Newborns Have Rights Also groups have won several cases concerning the rights of the newborn child and the apparent fault of the mother. Second, diet must be carefully controlled and nutrition balanced. As you can see, the meal that Mrs. Rubin... It is Rubin, isn't it? Your first name is—"

"Karol," I interrupted, "Go on, man. Go on."

"Yes, yes, yes."

I was getting more annoyed by the minute and the "yes, yes, yes" wasn't helping any.

"As you can see," he went on, "a dinner consisting of breaded veal cutlet, pasta, and potatoes is loaded with starch and doesn't contain enough vegetables or a balance of protein, fat, and carbohydrates. This is something we restaurateurs must be careful of today, because if an inspector is present, our license can be revoked. Also, if a federal or state official noticed Mrs. Rubin drinking Champagne or coffee in Villa Rosa's, we would be fined, and you would be asked to appear in court to defend your actions in jeopardizing your newborn infant."

"This is preposterous," I said, rising and pulling Karol with me.

"Preposterous, maybe," he continued, "but I would advise making an appointment with your obstetrician tomorrow so he can fill you in on other parts of the law. These, I believe, deal with allowable types of employment, smoking, and other potential hazards to the baby. As you can see, there is no smoking allowed in most public places today, for apparently the baby remains at risk."

"It seems to me," said Karol, obviously bewildered and upset, "that the unborn baby has begun to have more rights than the parents."

"Yes, yes, yes," came the reply. "Now before it gets too late, could I interest you in the zucchini squash?"

Submitted by Perinate
Happy Birthday To Who?

I recently sang "Happy Birthday To You" (donned an accordion as well) at the 40th anniversary of our NICU. Weeks later, repeated the task at my grandson's birthday party. Did you know that this ditty, written in the late 1800s was originally titled "Good Morning to All" and is probably the most performed song in the world? Now there is a dispute and a lawsuit where the following question has been raised: should this song should be part of the public domain (free access). Several years ago, a company charged a licensing fee for the song and the lawsuit asked the company to return all of the fees collected (over 2 million dollars/year). To demonstrate the interest in this topic there was a 68 page article published entitled "Copyright and the World's Most Popular Song". How did attorney discovery know how much to collect? I saw no cameras at the NICU or my grandson's party. Next up: Itsy Bitsy Spider Climbed Up the Water Spout.

The New York Times - June 14, 2013

Informed Consent
(Fall 1985)

The ringing of the phone could not even fully waken me, as my mouth was dry and my senses dull.

"Gene, it's me."

"Wha...? Who? Eeech... I just couldn't clear my throat. Suddenly my gut tightened as a sense of fear brought me to a more alert level.

"Gene, wake up. It's Gerri."

"What time is it? What's the matter? Are you OK?" The words ran out of my mouth, as I now was fully awake. "Gene, something is wrong with the baby. Dr. Iretolin just came to see me. The baby has periods where she just stops breathing. I'm so...so..."

"Hold on, honey. I'm getting dressed. I'll be there in twenty minutes."

As I washed my face and dressed, I thought about what Gerri had said. She had given birth to a seemingly healthy eight-pound baby only nine hours earlier. Her labor and delivery had been easy, and the baby seemed fine. The only problem with the whole procedure had been all the necessary paperwork, as clerks, nurses, doctors, and aides of all sorts had made us sign form after form about understanding side effects from medications, anesthesia, and all the possible things that could go wrong. This "informed consent" process was standard procedure so the doctor had said, but to me it had been a waste of time and a pain.

I finished dressing, grabbed my car keys, and left the house. Intervalley Hospital was only ten minutes away, but the ride seemed endless, even though there was little traffic. I had to use the emergency entrance and ran through the crowded hall to the staircase that led up to the maternity floor. The stairwell was brightly lit, and there were signs at each level.

USE THE HANDRAILS; PROCEED CAUTIOUSLY; SLOWER WALKERS KEEP TO THE LEFT; and WE ARE NOT RESPONSIBLE FOR ACCIDENTS were only a few of the signs I passed as I bounded up the stairs. Maternity was on the third floor. Opening the stairwell door and ignoring the LOOK BOTH WAYS warning, I ran to Gerri's room. The small light behind her outlined her hair, giving it an eerie appearance.

"Gene," she said, reaching for me, "I'm so glad you're here."

"It'll be all right, honey," I said, holding her close. "Now tell me again…what is so wrong?"

"The doctor says that Kari has periods where she stops breathing. They're trying to find out why. You'd better speak to him yourself. I think he's in the special…the special-care nursery."

"I'll go there right away. Do you feel strong enough to go? Perhaps you'd better stay here and rest."

"I want to go with you, but... Gene, I'm so..."

"Shh, shh... Let me hold you a second. Easy now. It'll be fine... I promise."

As I left Gerri, I felt bewildered, drained, and now afraid. I asked the nurse for directions to the special-care nursery, and she used the intercom to ask Dr. Iretolin to come out.

I waited only a few moments, and the door opened as a short, youngish-looking man in a yellow hospital gown walked out.

"Mr. West?"

I nodded.

"I'm Dr. Iretolin. Believe me, I'm sorry to bring you out at such a late hour, but I think it's important to talk to you about Kari." The doctor was obviously tired, but he had a gentle, understanding air about him. "Sit down with me a moment," he continued, guiding me to a chair in the anteroom. "Let me explain the situation to you."

"I don't understand this at all, Doctor. Kari was fine a few hours ago. What...just what can be so terribly wrong now?"

"Kari seemed fine at birth and several hours afterward. For some reason, however, she has had periods where she stops breathing. A certain number of these breathing lapses, called apnea, may be normal, but her pauses are becoming more frequent, and they are beginning to affect the rest of her system. We have to find out why these are occurring."

"What...what do you think she has? What can we do? Will you do something quickly?"

"Yes, yes, yes," he continued. "But Kari may have one problem or a combination of many problems. She may have sepsis, or infection, as you would call it. She might have low blood sugar or even something wrong with her heart. But in order for us to find out the reason, she needs to have blood tests, a spinal tap, x-rays, and possibly she may even need to be placed on a respirator in order to help her to breathe."

"OK, OK, whatever you want. But please hurry up, and let's get started. I want everything done as soon as possible."

"Yes, Mr. West. I understand your concern. But before we start testing or begin treatment, you must understand all the procedures and the risks involved and must sign a consent form for each and every procedure or medication."

"What? Again?" I asked, even more bewildered.

"I'm afraid so," continued Dr. Iretolin. "I'm sure the OB staff told you about the ICACMPSE process."

"The what?" I asked.

"The Informed Consent Act Concerning Medications, Procedures, and Side Effects." Congress passed this act in 1987 to try to curtail malpractice suits, which often developed years later. I'm sorry, but it's the law."

"Fine, fine. Tell me what to do or where to sign."

"I'm afraid it's not as simple as that. First you must understand the material, take a short exam that tests your knowledge, and then sign the form. Follow me to the Informed Consent Room."

Stupefied, I followed him down a short corridor to a gray door. We went inside, and in front of me was a long, narrow room with cubicles, each containing a videotape setup. Despite the late hour, the room was filled. Each cubicle had its own heading.

"Let's start here, Mr. West," said Dr. Iretolin.

I sat down in a chair as he turned on the video. In a moment the subject appeared. "The Spinal Tap Procedure" was printed on the screen. I sat through this tape and, in the next half hour, was subjected to a miniseries on antibiotics, apnea, and something called mechanical ventilation. My head was swimming.

"Now can I see Kari? I asked.

"Of course," said Dr. Iretolin. "Follow me. Wash your hands carefully for the full three required minutes."

After finishing, I followed the doctor into the nursery. The room was a beehive of activity, with beeping alarms and foreign sounds I never had heard before.

"Kari is over here, Mr. West."

I walked slowly to the incubator. Kari looked big compared to some of the other babies I had noticed, but she seemed pale under the bright lights. I shielded my eyes and looked at the baby.

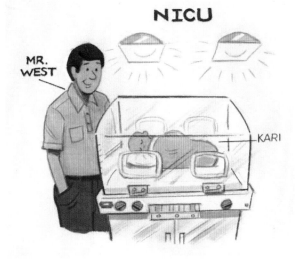

I heard Dr. Iretolin say to one of the nurses, "We must remember to dim the nursery lights. I understand that there's some evidence that a well-lighted nursery may lead to an increased incidence of retrolental fibroplasia. The lawyers will have a feast on that issue."

"What is retrolen… Well, anyway," I turned and asked Dr. Iretolin, "can you start treatment yet?"

"As soon as you sign all of the consent and freedom-from-liability forms. I have them right here."

The doctor produced a sheath of material, and I methodically signed them all, not really caring. *What the heck*, I said to myself. *These are only forms anyway.* I finished quickly and gave the material to Dr. Iretolin.

"Thank you, Mr. West," he said, smiling. "Now we can begin. Why don't you go downstairs and have a cup of coffee? I'll call you when we're done."

For the first time, I felt totally drained. *A cup of coffee might do me some good.* I decided to forego the stairs and take the elevator instead. The door opened, and there was an elevator operator seated on a small stool in the front. The musical sounds of Ella Fitzgerald singing "A Foggy Day" came from a small tape recorder in the corner.

"First floor, please," I said, as I walked inside. "Good morning, sir," was the answer. "Before we go down, however, I must tell you that there is a one in 7656 chance that we might experience a power failure in this elevator, and you must sign a consent form before we proceed."

"I must sign what?" I sputtered.

"It's all part of the legislation," he continued. "We cannot take a chance on your not understanding the risks involved in riding this elevator."

I looked up, took the offered pen, and signed.

"A foggy day in London town
had me low and had me down…"

Submitted by Perinate
Equalizing Payment Rates

The future seems clear. There will be fewer physicians working in private offices, and hospitals will shortly be the employer. The costs for patient visits and diagnostic tests are more expensive in the hospital setting (inpatient or outpatient) compared with physician offices and therefore there will be a negative effect on the Medicare budget. The administrators of the Centers for Medicare and Medicaid Services (CMS) support the general goal of "site-neutral payments". However, it is true that hospital costs involve many other expenses not experienced by the private physician office.

The Medicare Federal Advisory Panel advised decreasing payments to hospitals since many services can be provided at a cheaper rate in a doctor's office. Responses have been bipartisan, conflicting and confusing.

The legislation regarding reimbursement is immense, unclear and impossible for the consumer to understand. Before embarking on a "cutting scenario" perhaps it is necessary to first design a program which will be practical.

Robert Pear, New York Times
June 14, 2013

Hospital Choices
(Winter 1985)

I ran into my friend Griswald the other day as I was leaving the office. His face was red, and sweat dripped from his nose and eyeglasses. He was carrying three or four newspapers and seemed totally and hopelessly frazzled. "Hey, Gris," I said, grabbing his arm to get his attention. "Slow down a moment. What are you doing?"

"Oh! Hi, Paul," he said, looking up, as a big drop of sweat rolled from his nose to his upper lip. "My wife is in premature labor, and I have to quickly find a hospital where she'll be able to deliver safely."

"What's wrong with the hospital your doctor uses?" I asked.

"Well," he said with a shrug, "Logan Hospital closed down last year because of rising health costs and competition, and the nearest one remaining is twenty-four miles from home. Now the doctor tells me to look at the advertisements in the newspapers, as there are terrific savings since the government is allowing free enterprise and laissez-faire. Look at this," he said, pointing.

The advertisement read, "Have your preemie at Friendly Hospital. Two days of *free* incubator care, fifteen *free* blood-gas determinations, and two *free* total parenteral alimentation solutions with the attached coupon."

"That's nothing," continued Griswald. "There are eleven advertisements in today's paper, and the Sunday paper has three or four pages. Hospitaland's PPO advertisement is probably the best deal for the money, though. What do you think?"

In big print on the following page was an advertisement that read, "Hospitaland, the Total Facility for Perinatal Care." There were pictures of the hospital with attentive staff in white lab coats, but all the arrows pointed to the lower part of the page, where there were twenty-four coupons. These included discounts on fetal monitoring, episiotomies, and laxatives. There were "two-fors" for IVs, incubator days, and ventilators. There were free continental breakfasts and free room and board for one member of the family for three days and two nights if the mother and/or infant remained hospitalized.

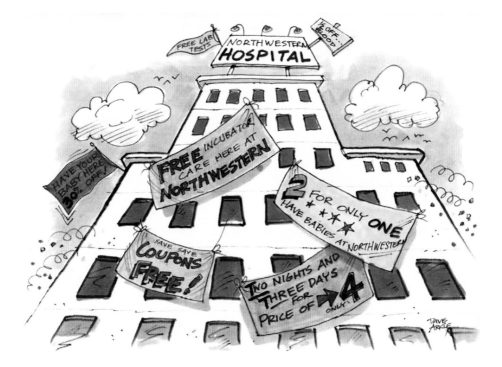

"Well, which should I choose? Griswald asked. "You've got a feel for this sort of thing. What would you do?"

"What are you doing, Gris?" I asked him. "Choosing a doctor and a hospital isn't the same thing as buying a car. When you buy a car, you choose the options you want, find out the prices, and bargain, since the products are equal. But there is no comparison when choosing a health-care facility or provider. You're not purchasing an item but buying a service you hope is the best. It cannot be judged in the same way as an appliance. Competition is price related in the consumer market when choosing manufactured items, but cannot be considered when you're looking for the best in a doctor. Your wife didn't want to go into premature labor, but now that she is in labor, you have to choose the best of all products, and price cannot be considered."

"Say, can I borrow your handkerchief, Paul?" Griswald continued, as he began to dab at his sweaty brow. "I guess you're right about choosing a doctor and hospital, and I'd better decide right now what's really best. But you must admit, two nights and three days really isn't a bad deal!"

Funding for Neonatology
(Spring 1986)

The news was not good. The government, facing an even larger deficit in 1994 than expected, was recommending another "austerity program." The expansion of the Star Wars defense system and the continual threat from orbiting foreign galactic pleopods allowed the administration to triple the defense budget at the expense of other programs. Although farming, education, and Social Security programs were axed initially, the health-care industry was now feeling the crunch. For the first time in the decade, fetal and neonatal mortality figures were rising, as there was not enough money to pay for personnel or needed equipment. Research was not funded; scientists were leaving the medical profession in droves; and the gloom-and-doom attitude was now a reality.

In August I was asked to join a select panel of neonatologists from the Perinatal Section of the American Academy of Pediatrics. A meeting was held in Washington, DC, and I noted that the American College of Obstetrics and Gynecology had sent delegates as well. After initial informal introductions and renewed hellos, we were asked to sit around an oblong table in a stately room near the Capitol. The twelve of us were an interesting bunch, I mused—three pediatricians, three neonatologists, three obstetricians, and three perinatologists. I noted, too, that not only were the seating arrangements such that the specialties were kept together, but also, within each group of three, there were well-defined age categories. It seemed that there was one physician in the 30-40 age category, one in the 41-50 range, and one in the 51- 60 range. *Probably a coincidence,* I thought, *but I wonder…*

"Ladies and gentlemen, I wonder if we might get down to business," began Dr. Eve Sordon, the president of the National Perinatal Coalition. "As you well know, Congress is about to pass the Kennedy-Glenn Bill, which will cut off federal funds for perinatal research, tighten the DRGs for perinatal medicine, and only allow tertiary or quaternary centers to operate. Since many of the old primary hospital centers closed in 1991 and 1992 much of the rural American population has been left without hospitals to care for both mother and infant, and inappropriate and unexpected home deliveries have increased. First, fetal and neonatal mortality increased. In the last six months, both maternal morbidity and mortality also have risen. The bottom line is money. We need to raise one hundred million dollars quickly to infuse into the system."

An immediate low-pitched buzzing was heard as the physicians reacted to Eve's statement.

"Eve," began Phil Gurman, one of the neonatologists, "isn't this a bit out of our league? We're physicians, not fund-raisers or legislators. I'm sure Polly and Saul would also agree."

"Hold on a minute, Phil," Eve said. "Look around the room at the other people who are on this committee. All of you have something in common. You were chosen not only because of your expertise in your particular field, but also because every person in this room has a secondary talent that can be used to help raise the money."

I looked around again. *No oil money here*, I thought. *I don't see any fancy jewelry, and I can't remember limousines downstairs. Ordinary dress with gray slacks and blue blazers... No Bijan silk suits to be found.*

Eve motioned for quiet again. "It's time to explain," she said. "Each of you has either been a professional athlete, musician, actor, or actress before becoming a physician. Since all the big money today resides in these three fields, we would like to set up a big athletic event, like a Super-Super Bowl XXIII. At halftime many famous people would come onto the field, join hands, and sing a song that would be flashed on the screen and sung by everyone. The song would be so full of nationalism and feeling that it would then be recorded and sold in the stores, and the profits from the game and the records would make up the deficit."

Everyone thought of the same thing. In 1984 "We Are the World" made millions for the people in Africa. In 1986 "Hands Across America" sold eighteen million records and brought in eighty million dollars.

The buzz returned.

"It could work," said Refrigerator Perry. "I could ask some of my old buddies to help."

"Bill," I said, "are any of the old *Cosby Show* people around? We might get NBC to take television rights."

There was great excitement in the room. Dates, times, places, and ideas were all thrown out for discussion and either discarded or agreed upon. The final questions dealt with who should write and record the song. The older group wanted Sinatra or Streisand. The middle group opted for Manilow or Diamond. The younger group only wanted Springsteen, "The Boss."

Finally Eve called for attention. "Please, please," she began. "All this arguing over *who* and *how* will do us no good. We have among us someone who has experience in the recording business and who would be perfect."

Her gaze turned to me, and all eyes followed. "Perry, you write and record the song."

On October 15, 1994, the event was held in the new 180,000-seat American Stadium. The song, "Let Our Babies Grow," brought tears to the eyes of all people everywhere. During the first twelve weeks of production, the song, written and performed by Perry Nate, was at the top of all Billboard charts.

The rest…is history.

"Let Our Babies Grow"
Words and Music by Perry Nate

Verse

In this day and age,
we often wonder why.
Seems there is no greater sound
than a newborn baby's cry.

It means an early start,
which hopefully will last.
The cry looks to be the future
and wipes away the past.

Chorus

Give us the heart and hope
to let our babies grow.
Make sure the care is such,
so we are in the know.
Let our babies grow with love.
Allow them all this chance.
Watch them coo and talk
and walk.
Watch them run and dance.

Verse

Knowledge, care, and money
will help our babies' cause.
Stand up tall. Ask for all.
Break down these closed doors.

Don't allow a very few
to spoil it for the rest.
America must take the step.
Its kids deserve the best.

Chorus

Give us the heart and hope
to let our babies grow.
Make sure the care is such,
so we are in the know.
Let our babies grow with love.
Allow them all this chance,
Watch them coo and talk
and walk.
Watch them run and dance.

Liability
(Summer 1986)

I came into the nursery,
to start my morning rounds.
And felt a strange sensation,
I didn't hear the sounds.

The beeps, the whirrs, the pings, and clicks,
that made the staff all rush.
Were replaced by simple silence,
an eerie sort of hush.

A Timely Scenario

Nurses bagging babes by hand,
Uusing auscultation….
Charting heart and breathing rates,
is this called cerebration?

"What goes on?," I said to Sue,
team Leader of the day.
"Plug in all the monitors,
and let's start on our way."

"Perinate," she said so fast,
"it's not all up to me.
The problem goes much further;
called liability.

The Bird has raised its premium,
to cover all the cost.
And left us bagging all the kids,
the battle has been lost.

"We cannot use these instruments,
or plug them in their sockets.
Until the government reacts,
to stifle these "deep pockets."

"Co-defendants, cross-complaints,
to me it seems so lame.
Mental anguish, negligence,
who will take the blame?

"The doctors feel the courts unjust,
as lawyers earn their fee.
Based upon a trumped-up deal,
known as contingency.

Liability

"Costs are high—, there is no doubt,
I'm sorry, if I'm short.
My hands are cramping, neck so stiff,
someone must change the "tort."

"O.K," I said. , "Let's isolate,
but first please close the door.
Bring back all the instruments,
we'll somehow self-insure."

Common sense should soon prevail,
it is a bitter pill.
Let's hear the beeps, the whirrs, the clicks,
and send the courts the bill.

Submitted by Perinate
Rules for Abortion: Fetal Pain Theory

A growing number of States are changing their legislation concerning when abortions can be performed. These laws are banning abortions at 20 weeks based on the fact that the "fetus" is capable of feeling pain. The anti-abortion groups are very vocal in determining a "Right-to-Life" campaign to uphold a 20 week ban on performing abortions. The science is confusing. Reactions to noxious stimuli probably cannot occur without nerve connections between the cortex and thalmus. Embryologically most thalamocortical fibers appear between 23-30 weeks. Can there be functional pain perception? A confounding factor is also the concept of viability. We are now saving babies of lower gestational age and it is common to resuscitate babies at 22 weeks and above even though if mortality is prevented, severe morbidity is not. Science and constitutional law are in controversy. The answer may lie in future studies defining when the perception of fetal pain is real.

Theory on Pain is Driving Rules for Abortion. Erik Eckholm, New York Times 8/2/13.

Valpractice
(Fall 1986)

"And so, members of the jury, I want you to look again at two-year-old Indiana Nicol, who, although born prematurely at 32 weeks of pregnancy, is perfectly normal today. This accomplishment was part of the team effort demonstrated by both the perinatal and neonatal health-care network, but Indiana's recovery from the most serious part of his illness was the result of the better care offered by Dr. Bunshine, compared to that of Dr. Adamkind. Now, look into your hearts…your souls…and render a valpractice judgment in favor of Dr. Bunshine."

Allen Margol turned slowly away from the jury. His movements were well practiced. Taking small steps, he passed the bench, nodded to me, and gracefully sat down.

As the judge in this case, I stifled a yawn, trying to appear professional, but was bored out of my mind. Today's schedule was full of these valpractice cases. The pendulum was swinging full circle, and things finally would get back to normal…but when? The malpractice crisis had reached its peak in 1987, when, after three judgments of more than $30 million, all the insurance carriers had quit. Doctors converted their assets, hospitals set up trusts and foundations, and suddenly there was no money for patients or their lawyers. The most litigious law firms in the country began to experience financial problems, and the public complained about "due process." They were right. For a period of time, there was no process. Finally, in 1988, someone—to this day I can't remember who—coined the term "valpractice." The expression was an abbreviation for "value in practice," and it rewarded the individual for the extra effort, the correct decision. In simple terms it substituted "val" for "mal." Before long the rules became extremely complicated. A panel at each hospital was created to determine whether "your care was better than my care." Points were offered to doctors for better judgment, extra time spent with families, quality and penmanship of patient notes, use of medications, and so forth.

This initial group of criteria soon expanded as nurses, social workers, and respiratory therapists became involved. A "point guard" was added to each hospital unit to assist in the judgment process.

The snowball continued. Doctors and nurses no longer had time to use handwritten notes, as the entries in the charts were voluminous. The medical record office soon ran out of room and personnel. Typing pools were enlarged immediately, and in fact the stock of TPI (Typing Pools International), a small company that had gone public on the over-the-counter exchange on June 27th at six dollars a share, had split twice and was still twelve dollars a share by September 18th. Hospitals changed their building plans and converted patient rooms into storage facilities for charts, typewritten reports, and copying machines. A new industry was formed.

The competition was fierce. Doctors wanted to work extra hours in order to spend more time with patients and their families to rack up valpractice points. Nurses took double shifts, and one ICN nurse in Cleveland broke the nursing work record by doing a "triple-double."

Library and research staff members were overwhelmed with requests for literature searches, as doctors proved their extra value with references and more references. The lawyers were ecstatic. The insurance companies reappeared, quoting valpractice insurance and offering a part of the judgment to the family if something occurred that was of lesser value. That is, nothing was described in terms of malpractice or poor care any longer. If an error occurred, it was thought of in terms of being of "lesser value" than someone else's care.

Before long the inevitable occurred. The court calendar became overcrowded, and it often took two to three years for a case to come to trial. The competition between self-interest groups eroded the team effort, and perinatal and neonatal mortality rates increased. It was obvious that a new type of tort reform was needed.

My reverie was broken as the jury returned to the courtroom.

"Thank you, ladies and gentlemen," I began. "Have you reached a verdict?"

"We have, Your Honor," replied the foreperson, a heavyset woman with thick red eyeglasses. "The jury would especially like to thank the respiratory therapist expert witnesses provided by both doctors for clearly explaining the basic functions of the current equipment available. In fact..." she continued. *On with it*, I thought. "...several members of the jury are considering leaving their present fields of work and returning to school to become respiratory therapists."

"Please, please," I interrupted. "May the court have the verdict?"

"Of course. I am sorry, Your Honor. The jury felt that Dr. Bunshine had demonstrated great value to the patient on the third day, when oxygenation had failed and all respirator changes had produced no improvement in the blood gases or clinical status. He changed to the Ultrasonic Clark Company Friction ventilator, and Indiana suddenly improved. For this reason we find Dr. Bunshine guilty of valpractice. In addition we believe that Dr. Adamkind should be remanded for additional education courses focusing on the Ultrasonic Clark Company Friction ventilator."

"Thank you for your time and effort. The jury is dismissed, and this case is closed."

As the reporters scurried out of the courtroom to phone in the verdict, I wondered whether a call to my broker about the Ultrasonic Clark Company would be considered insider information.

Instead, I picked up the phone. "Hello, hello… Phyllis? I'll be home in thirty minutes for lunch."

Submitted by Perinate
Informed Consent - Watchdog

Informed consent refers to consent by a patient to a surgical procedure, medical procedure or participation in a clinical study after an understanding of the relevant medical facts and the risks involved.

The "watchdog office" of the Federal office for Human Research Protection is considering action against the University of Alabama at Birmingham for not adequately informing parents about risks to their premature infants when enrolling in the Support Trial. This study was designed to discover levels of oxygen concentration administered to premature infants to pinpoint the level at which the risk of eye damage or neurological damage would occur.

We deal with informed consent on a daily basis. Have you ever read the insert provided by a drug company? The information is extensive and exhaustive.

Physicians and other healthcare professionals should decide the proper amount of information which constitutes informed consent.

By the time the family is informed of the purpose, methods, procedures, benefits and risks they will lose sight of the principal objective. We need a more reasonable approach.

Jan Hoffman, The New York Times June 5th, 2013

DRG Relocation
(Winter 1986)

"Good morning. This is the Neonatal DRG Relocation Center. Can I help you?"

"Dr. Bernfrank, please. I am trying to reach Dr. S. Bernfrank."

"One moment please," was the answer. "I'll ring."

"S.B., there's a call for you on one."

"Who is it, Donna?" I replied.

"There is a Dr. Alexi Kaiservitch who wants to talk to you. It sounds long distance, and he sounds impatient."

"Fine, fine, but send Andrea in. I might need her to take some notes." *Kaiservitch…Kaiservitch,* I thought. *Should I know the name?*

"Hello. This is Dr. Bernfrank. How may I help you?"

"Is this Dr. S. Bernfrank, the Director of the Neonatal DRG Relocation Center?"

The voice seemed throaty and harsh. The words were rushed, almost clipped; the accent slightly foreign but practiced.

"Yes, yes," I replied. Although intrigued, I was getting a little impatient. The static on the line made hearing him even more difficult.

"Good, good," was the reply. "I am Dr. Alexi Kaiservitch, Assistant Director to the Health Organization of the KGB."

"The what?"

"The KGB, the Soviet Union—"

"I know, I know," I interrupted. "Are you calling from Russia?"

"No, actually I am in San Diego. The director of our subsection was interested in this DRG Relocation Center of yours and asked me to contact you—to set up a meeting, or as you say, an appointment. How do you Americans put it…? Can we do lunch? You see, the KGB wants to learn about the DRG."

This must be a joke, I thought. *Not bad…not bad. Who could be doing this? I'll play along a bit longer.*

"Donna," I said through the intercom, "ask Andrea if I can clear some time later this afternoon."

Andrea had been standing in the doorway through the whole conversation. She smiled, nodded yes, and shrugged her shoulders while winking at the same time. *How does she do that?* I thought.

"Fine, fine," I continued. "Why don't you drop by about four o'clock this afternoon?"

"Yes, good, good, yes. I will see you then."

I spent the rest of the morning making the usual trades between the hospitals in my area that were part of the DRG system. There were no emergencies, and deals were quite routine. At exactly four o'clock, Andrea knocked on the door and ushered in Dr. Alexi Kai-servitch. I had expected a paunchy, squat, balding man in a gray wool suit with three-inch cuffs. Instead, standing in front of me was a thin, willowy, fiftyish man dressed in San Diego seersucker. He strode briskly across the room and offered his hand.

Obviously an actor, I thought, as I extended my own hand. We both pumped up and down, embarrassed, not knowing when to stop.

I finally broke free. "Please sit down Dr. Kaiservitch," I said.

"Thank you, Dr. Bernfrank."

"You can call me S.B. Everyone else does."

"Then you should call me Alex," he said with a smile. "No one else does."

We both laughed and, as with the handshake, didn't know when to stop. He suddenly reached down to pick up his briefcase, which was on his right side. He placed the briefcase on his lap, opened it so that I wasn't able to see what he was doing, and shuffled some papers.

Ah, now it comes, I thought. *Roses are red. Violets are...*

"In case you wondered about me, here are my credentials."

He passed me a paper with official-looking seals and stamps. *This can't be serious, can it?* I said to myself. *If it is, do I need a special type of clearance? What the hell do I do now?* Not wanting to appear insecure or not in control of the situation, I decided to continue with this charade.

"This page seems fine to me, Doctor—I mean, Alex," I said. "What can I do for you?"

"As I said on the phone, the Soviet Union is very interested in the health-care delivery system used by the Americans. We are looking for a model, especially in—how you say—newborn medicine. We want to start with something correct and not make all the mistakes you Americans have made. Am I not right?"

"Oh, then you're a neonatologist or a perinatologist?"

"No, no. I'm an orthodontist. The newborn people are so busy that they couldn't send anyone else. Now, to begin, please tell me about how this relocation center was started."

"Fine, fine," I said. "I'll make it as simple as possible. 'DRG' stands for Diagnostic Related Group. This is a system in which patients are admitted to the hospital and are listed under categories that specify hospital reimbursement. There are many DRGs for newborn care. I'll provide you with this classification. A specific number of days are assigned to each DRG, and this is the number of days that the infant can stay in the hospital. If the baby is discharged before the DRG criteria are met, the hospital makes money. If the infant stays longer, the hospital loses money. There are certain extension-of-time models called 'outliers' that can extend the number of days, but all in all, it's a simple system. It only gets out of hand if one hospital is overloaded with patients that exceed the DRGs. This can lead to bankruptcy. This has happened many times this year. My job is to assist the system by relocating babies from one place to another so that the hospitals stay in business.

"Come with me now. It's almost five o'clock. The nurses are now on twelve-hour shifts, and they like to arrange for transfers so that the next group handles the work. It's the same everywhere. Watch your step as we enter the room I call 'the pit.' "

"Why do you do this type of thing, S.B.?" Dr. Kaiservitch asked.

"You see, I was a practicing neonatologist for fifteen years. I became so frustrated with the system, the administrative crap, and the economics, that I wanted to quit. As a young man working my way through college, I had some experience in the Chicago hog market, so I was a natural for this type of job. Come with me. I'll show you."

Dr. Kaiservitch looked at me as if he didn't understand a word. *If this guy is genuine,* I thought, *I'd better get some type of permission.* Who would I call? I made up the conversation in my mind.

"Hello, this is the Department of Health, Education, and Welfare. Can I help you?" said a sweet voice.

"Thank you. This is Dr. S. Bernfrank, Director of the Neonatal DRG Relocation Center in California. Can I speak with the Secretary, please? No, not you, I mean the Secretary of Health, Education, and Welfare, Dr. Joshi. You need more information before putting me through to him? Well, this afternoon a man claiming to be from the KGB came to see me about...."

What a dumb story! They would never believe me.

The noise of the phones cleared my head. The term "the pit" described the area where we were now standing. There were three large consoles, with one phone and four separate channels located on each console. In the center was a NASA-looking electronic display board where all the hospitals were depicted with different colored lights. The number of NICU beds, types of patients, used outlier days, and the number of days still available were presented for each hospital. It was the operator's function to determine the number of days available, to compare this number with the patients already in house, and to project what would happen if other admissions occurred. The operators passed slips of paper to Andrea and Donna, and they gave these facts to me. The unit directors would call me, and I would be able to tell them if they had to give up, or accept patients or what their current status was concerning admissions. There was a specially designated red DRG phone in each NICU, and the Directors would call me with their problems.

A Timely Scenario

The phones were ringing, and I momentarily forgot about Dr. Kaiservitch. The slips started coming quickly, and I used the computer to calculate the money. Although there were only eleven hospitals in my area, I had been told that the pit resembled an airport control tower and that the tension level was like that of an air traffic controller.

I was sweating as I realized that Presbyterian Hospital was in a jam, and I needed to get rid of three patients, but fast! *Let's see*, I thought. *Kaiser Hospital is slow today...*

I dialed quickly.

"Hi, Bart... Good, good. This is Bernfrank. You're overstuffed. You need to transfer the kid with PFC, the BPD patient, and even one of the twins. I can send two full-term kids tomorrow, which will put you ahead. OK, OK, I'll arrange it. Thanks."

I hung up quickly and picked up the next phone.

"Jay, it's me. You're OK right now, but if you get a 1:1 or 2:1 admission, we may have to make a trade. Keep in touch."

"S.B.," Donna said, "pick up on one. It's Dr. U.A. Line from the center."

"U.A., S.B. What can I do for you?"

"S.B., I need your help. I discharged four kids today. No new admissions. The nurses are floating. They are floating. Do you know what that means? The administration is telling them not to come in for the next shift. The unit director is not smiling at me. She's yelling. Do something!"

"Not to worry, U.A.," I said with a smile. "I'll take two from Rich Pearl at Children's. A piece of cake."

"Thanks, S.B., I owe you one."

Boy, this was the front line! Catheters, ET tubes, pneumothoraces—nothing could compare with this excitement. My shirt was soaked.

"Dr. S. B.! Dr. S.B.!

I turned. It was Kaiservitch. In the heat of the battle, I had forgotten all about him.

"Very impressive, S.B.!" he said.

When did he get so friendly? I thought.

"This system would do well in my country. But I do have one question. The parents… What about them?"

"What do you mean?" I said.

"Well, what happens if they like a particular NICU or doctor or nurse? You Americans call it 'bonding.' What if they want to stay in that particular facility? Furthermore what if they live so far away that it would be difficult to visit their child if you transferred the baby to another place? What can they do?"

I didn't blink an eye. My answer was preschooled and packaged.

"Dr. K," I said, "there is no DRG for compassion. The times have changed. You can no longer think of an individual patient or family. You must look at the entire picture, the whole state rather than the…"

What am I saying? I thought Here I was, an American, proud of my individual rights and proud of the best health-care system in the world, when actually I was working in a collective system much like the one in which my foreign colleague belonged.

"Excuse me a moment," I said.

I bounded up the stairs, ran into my office, and picked up the phone. Shaking, I dialed the number.

"Hello, this is the Department of Health, Education, and Welfare. How can I help you?"

"This is Dr. S. Bernfrank, Director of the Neonatal DRG Relocation Center in California. I must speak with the Secretary..... Now!"

Is It One or Two?
(Spring 1987)

A beautiful day, mused Mary Jo Babin, as she turned right onto the freeway. She automatically pushed the left-turn signal and slowly merged with the traffic flow. Her rear computer beeped, warning her that a car was approaching on her left. The mirrors automatically adjusted, and the dashboard computer flashed the approaching car's speed, along with Mary Jo's speed and the correction necessary to avoid a collision.

It's almost four o'clock, she thought. *Why was Dr. Pomoakes so late? Obstetricians certainly have a knack for keeping patients waiting. I wonder how much traffic will slow me down.*

As she passed the freeway flashboard, she noted that it read, Fastrack Lane. Sorry—Computer Down. Consult Laser Disc Radio.

Mary Jo turned on the disc system and said in a loud, clear voice, "News, please. 104.2 AM."

"Thank you," said a mechanical voice from the front speaker. "Will continue to check for a news station."

A moment later the static was gone, and a polished voice said, "This is Alixandra Nitram of *104.2 News.* Give us twenty minutes, and we'll give you an hour."

I've heard her say this for months, thought Mary Jo, and *I still don't know what it means.*

Alixandra continued, "The President today apologized for the six-percent surtax but explained that the previous administration had ignored the deficit, and there was no other way to prevent recession except to raise taxes and add a surcharge. In other news Dr. W. Lierson of the NIH announced that the number of AIDS cases has continued to decrease since the vaccine has been widely used. Due to the medical-legal complications with vaccine-induced injury claims, the vaccine companies have been slow to produce the material. The President's Task Force is working on this problem. And now, 104.2 Sports."

Noting that the traffic was increasing, Mary Jo said, "Slow down. Adjust speed to traffic flow."

The computer made the adjustment, and the car slowed.

I hope technology can one day devise a system so that I won't have to steer or move from lane to lane, Mary Jo thought.

She rested her hand on her abdomen and smiled as she felt the baby kick. Dr. Pomoakes had confirmed that she was six months pregnant, and she was taking the ultrasound tape home to show Howie.

The traffic was much heavier now, and she looked for the commuter lane, which appeared several hundred yards ahead. Cars were already moving to the left to enter this faster section. She set her left blinker and said, "Accelerate." She steered left, and the automatic-guidance system did the rest. The sign above the point read, COMMUTER CARPOOL LANE—2 OR MORE.

Mary Jo entered the lane and smiled as she passed cars on her right that were stuck in traffic. After driving for several miles, as she thought about the baby's room and what to make for dinner, the computer's speaker belched and stopped her thoughts.

"There are flashing lights behind you. There are flashing lights behind you. Probabilities are the police, an ambulance, or a motorcycle gang."

Mary Jo felt her heartbeat quicken as she looked in the rearview mirror. *It's the police all right. What did I do wrong?*

"Slow down," said Mary Jo, as she steered to the right shoulder of the road. The car obeyed the command, slowed, and finally stopped after the next verbal order.

Mary Jo waited in the car as the officer approached. She rolled down her window and said, "Good afternoon, Officer. Did I do something wrong? I know I wasn't speeding."

CARPOOL LANE
2 OR MORE !

"No, ma'am," was the answer. "The sign says, 'Two or more,' and I only see one of you in the car."

"Oh, Officer, can't you see that I'm six months pregnant? In fact I'm on my way home from the obstetrician."

"Please get out of the car, ma'am. You don't look six months pregnant to me."

Mary Jo opened the door as the policeman moved away. She stepped out and faced him. The traffic, heavier now, whizzed around them.

"Nope. I'm sorry, ma'am. You don't look six months pregnant. The law says that if the baby is at more than five months' gestation, it counts as a person, and you can use the commuter lane. I don't think you're telling me the whole truth...looks closer to four months, I would say."

"Do you want to feel the baby move?" asked Mary Jo.

"Oh, I don't think so."

"Wait, wait. I've got an idea. I have my ultrasound tape with me. It's dated today, and you'll be able to see that I'm six months pregnant."

Not another ultrasound evaluation, thought the policeman. *I had so much trouble with that stuff at the academy.* "OK, OK," he conceded. "Hand over the tape."

Mary Jo reached into the car, removed the tape, and handed it to the man.

"I'll be back in a minute," he said. "Get back in the car and wait."

He returned to his car, sat down, and placed the tape in the laser VCR recorder. Then he removed a small book with pictures and graphs from a compartment below the recorder.

Let's see, he thought. *Find the head first. OK, now hold that position.* After he pressed the BD (biparietal diameter) button, the computer printout read, 63 mm. He checked the crown-rump length, abdominal circumference, and femur length as well. The computer informed him that the gestation age of the baby was 25 weeks.

I'll be damned, he thought. *She was telling the truth.*

The officer removed the tape from the VCR, got out of his car, and headed toward Mary Jo.

Seeing his approach, she rolled down the window.

"Sorry, ma'am. I guess you just look kinda small to me. I'll write you a note so if you're stopped again you won't have to waste so much time."

"Thank you, Officer. I'd really appreciate that. My husband and I are supposed to make a seven o'clock movie tonight."

Mary Jo took the hastily written note, looked in the rearview mirror, started the car, and said, "Accelerate, and move into the traffic flow." She steered, and the computer and car did the rest.

Later that evening, Howie and Mary Jo stood in line at the Tele-Pix 10 Theater.

"Two tickets for *Rambo* 11," said Howie.

Is It One or Two?

"That will be twenty-two dollars," answered the movie clerk.

"Thank you," said Howie, as he took the tickets.

They walked to the front and gave the usher their tickets. He took the tickets and looked at Mary Jo carefully. "Ma'am, could you step over here please?"

"Wha...what's the matter?" she asked.

"You only gave me two tickets, and to me it's obvious that there are three of you. Your husband will need to buy another ticket for the baby."

The rest...is history.

Submitted by Perinate
Sleep Sacks in the Nursery

Over the years pediatricians have recommended stomach sleeping, side sleeping and recently back sleeping as information concerning SIDS revealed that the incidence decreased with a back sleeping protocol.

So now we are presented with "sleep sacks". These sleep sacks give babies more freedom of leg movement, makes swaddling safer and supposedly gives babies a more secure feeling. These products are often offered free to hospitals with the hope that parents will purchase them when the baby goes home. Experienced nurses have prided themselves for generations in their swaddling techniques. They may not be happy about these new sleep sacks. I predict there will be a trend to increase use of the sleep sacks, followed by an accident when the sleep sack is too close to the nose or mouth leading to a suffocation type incident.

A randomized double blind trial would certainly be a welcome investigation by these companies before a product is placed in the market.

Laura Landro. A Better Night's Sleep for All. The Wall Street Journal, May 14, 2013.

Ode to Surrogation
(Summer 1987)

The United States of America,
A proud, progressive nation.
Has become deeply involved,
In maternal surrogation.

A contact was drawn up, you see,
In simple terms, to please.
Now attorneys and magistrates,
Have added LEGALESE.

This issue, friends, is not that new,
With no concern for libel.
Hagar bore Abraham a son,
It says so in the Bible.

No notes were drawn, no cash did pass,
The deal lacked compensation.
Sarah was miffed, however, at Hagar's
Successful incubation.

Centuries passed, the practice grew,
With gold-and-diamond purses.
In Dickens' day, infants were fed,
By loving gals…wet nurses.

A Timely Scenario

Governesses, adoptive parents,
All have roles to play.
It's no wonder, that we've reached,
This quandary of today.

Renting space to nurture life,
Artificial insemination.
No different in a Petri dish,
Or test-tube procreation.

WOMB 4 RENT

Ethical considerations,
Are legally complex.
It's not surprising that these techniques,
Have obfuscated sex.

The agreement of the service type,
Like one you'd buy at Sears.
The contract is not for Baby M,
So why then all the tears?

Ode to Surrogation

The answer lies within emotions,
The psyche that governs all.
Separation after bonding,
Mom hears her baby bawl.

This problem will not go away;
Support groups now add style.
They've made a biological process,
Become quite mercantile.

Surrogate Mothers Limited,
A business with a range.
Has offered shares to new investors,
On the OTC exchange.

A Timely Scenario

First will come the legal statutes,
Then full-blown legislation.
As supply and demand do flux,
There will be regulation.

The industry will progress, I'm sure,
Profits and laissez-faire.
Finally forced to de-regulate,
The public will see air.

A cottage industry born in Genesis,
Though technically, no sweat.
Has now become child bartering,
Or, "Whose kid will you get?"

We cannot separate human feelings,
From contractual restitution.
Back to basics…consultation,
The U.S. Constitution.

Leprosy and AIDS
(Fall 1987)

October 3, 1885
Molokai, Hawaii

Dear Poppa,

I have been on this island for six months now and only have had time today to write you this letter. How I miss everyone at home. When I was first diagnosed with the disease, I was so ashamed. The church thought I was spiritually as well as physically unclean. The doctors and the priests made me undress, and they examined me from head to toe. I remember they paid so much attention to my skin and the sensations on my hands and feet—and so much time on my mouth.

What were they looking for? I kept asking myself. Afterwards, they took away my clothes and gave me a small rattle. Every time I saw another person, I was to shake the rattle to warn of my approach. I was never to touch anything with my hands, and for weeks I had to wear gloves. There were so many others like me that we stayed together, only entering the towns on the special days that were allowed by law. Then, when our numbers grew, we were all taken off the streets and placed into special hospitals, where no other type of patient was allowed—only those stricken. Finally, as I told you in my letter before leaving, the government became afraid, thinking that this "plague-like illness" might continue to spread. All the hospitals were emptied, and within days we were placed aboard ships and taken to this island called Molokai.

A Timely Scenario

The island itself is beautiful, almost thirty-eight miles long and seven miles wide. There are high mountains and great cliffs. In 1873, when the first colony was started, the people lived in grass huts or even under trees. There was no sanitation, food was poor, and there was almost no medical help. Much of this has changed now because of Father Damien and Brother Joseph. Poor Father Damien. He came down with the disease several years ago and is getting worse. His skin ulcers are rampant, and he coughs all day long, as if he has consumption. Bless him, though, for he has given so much to our colony. Brother Joseph has taken over many of the duties to care for us. Here, there is the principle "*Aole kanawai ma keia wahi,*" which means "In this place there is no law." All of us know we are dying, it is only a matter of time. I was lucky to be placed in the Monty House. It is a home built near the steamer landing. Only girls live here, and at least I have my own cot and linens.

I have been more frightened the last few days. I spilled some hot water on my foot and didn't feel the pain. Also the skin around my ears seems to be thicker, and some tell me that my face is changing. Last week I took the *Goto* treatment, which consisted of hot baths and special medications. I have not felt different yet. There is talk of a new medicine called *chaulmoogra* oil. It is very hard to get, and I understand that the government will not make it easily available to us. *Why?* I wonder.

I should end this letter now, as twilight comes, and soon the candles will be lit. I fear I never shall see you or the rest of the family again. My eventual disfigurement and personal shame will only make it harder for you. I thank you for all the love and support you provided. I surely would have died without your love and help. Please write to me. If you hear of a new medicine or anything that would help our colony, write to Brother Joseph. He is truly one of the Samaritans of Molokai.

Your daughter,
Rebecca

A Timely Scenario

October 3, 1995
Molokai, Hawaii

Dear Pops,

How ya doing? I know it's been six months since you last heard from me, but believe me, the time has been a real bummer. When the antibody test first came back positive, I said to myself, *Not to worry. It will take years before something happens.* But then came the new regulations. It was like I had the plague. I was even fired from my job. In desperation I went to see Father Angelo. He couldn't help me, except to send me to a "support center." The social workers were helpful, but everyone seemed so afraid.

The doctors at the clinic saw me every month. They examined me from head to toe. They paid gobs of attention to my feet, neck, and mouth. I do have some sores around my ankles that they call ulcers. Finally they gave me this card and said I must show it at all times, when I'm eating at restaurants or even when I'm outside. They also gave me these large rubber gloves and told me I must always wear them before touching anything or anyone. Soon there were so many of us that almost everyone had cards and wore gloves. The government took us off the streets and placed us in specially designated hospitals. But the hospitals were soon filled, and the legislators felt this "plague-like illness" might continue. Within days the hospitals were emptied, and we were placed on planes and taken to this island called Molokai.

The island is a gas. I'm told it's about thirty-eight miles long and seven miles wide. Mountains and cliffs are everywhere. There's a swimming pool that has a bar in it. I'm staying at a place called the Monty House. Three girls and I share a two-bedroom condo.

There are plenty of things to do on the island—tennis, golf, and even snorkeling. But when you get sicker, they take you to a separate hospital-type area. There are nurses who come to each condo to give IV medications and to change "nutritional catheters." Here there's the principle "*Aole kanawai ma keia wahi,*" which means "in this place there is no law." All of us know we are dying, it is only a matter of time.

I have coughed more the last few days and notice that some of the swellings I first had in my neck have enlarged. The ulcers on my feet seem larger too. I've been taking a new medication called CPA 1000, but I haven't noticed an improvement yet. There's talk of a new medicine or even a vaccine, but I hear that the FDA just won't move on these new therapies. *Why?* I wonder.

I should sign off now, as I'm late for aerobics class. I probably will never see you guys again. I know I'm infectious to others, like a "Typhoid Mary," but there's nothing I can do. I do thank you for sending me the "bread" I needed to get through the first few weeks. The help and emotional support also were great. There is a dude here from the church named Father D, who has provided us with love and support. If you can get the big boys from the FDA off their butts to let us have experimental drugs, let him know. This guy is truly one of the Samaritans of Molokai.

Later,
Becky

Tomb of Amenhotep
(Winter 1987)

1987—Tomb of Amenhotep (Akhenaton)
Valley of The Kings, Egypt

Bruce Bindel, tired from two hours of bending and crawling, stretched to restore the circulation in his lower legs.

"Joel, we're almost there. I can feel it."

"I hope so, Bindel" was the reply. "I'm beginning to think the last few months of struggle haven't been worth it. Hey, I feel a draft coming from the right. Do you?'

Turning to the right, Joel loosened the limestone around him and groped a supporting wall. He felt smooth plaster and then the seal of what he hoped was Amenhotep's tomb. The passage was clearer now, and both men were able to crouch. Their headlights glared, splitting the darkness and producing eerie shadows.

"Bindel, I'm sure this is it. The tomb of Amenhotep IV!"

Six months earlier Stanford University had hired both men to locate this tomb. An earlier discovery had led archeologists to believe that in his later years Amenhotep had built a small city to the east of the great Amon at Karnak. This medically oriented city had none of the anthropomorphic representations of the deities but by legend was supposed to have tried a scientific approach to life and sickness. There was an emphasis upon "*maat*," truth as determined by the king, with exclusion of the high priests. The city, called Akhetaton Nor, was destroyed after a few years, as Smenkhroy, who reigned from 1364 to 1361 BC, did not believe in the experiment, and Nefertiti, who had supported the project with Amenhotep, had died. Texts from Armana spoke of this city in high praise. During that period the number of deaths from illness (especially in childbirth and in the first few weeks of life) decreased significantly.

1987 - VALLEY OF THE KINGS
AMENHOTEP'S TOMB, EGYPT

Both men made quick work of the mortar that held the stone blocks in front of the tomb. A large block cracked after one chisel blow and fell forward, landing with a thud on the floor of the chamber beyond. The men widened the entrance and crawled through. The aroma of incense and cedar sharpened their instincts.

The walls were rough. There were many chests in the small room, and one had a beautiful image on its surface. It depicted the Pharaoh Amenhotep surrounded by bouquets of lotus and poppies carrying an infant. The images were continuous and filled the top of the trunk and the sides. The infant, originally carried by the Pharaoh, was first given to a young woman robed in white and finally placed in a small cubicle.

"Bruce, this is the chest we've been looking for. Give me the chisel and mallet."

After a few deft, hard strokes, the lock gave way.

Joel turned up the fluorescent light and opened the lid. He expected to hear squeaks and creaks as the lid was opened but was surprised at the silence. "Bindel," he said, "look at this."

There were three ox-bone-handled daggers on top of a papyrus scroll. Squatting, Joel reached into the chest, pushed the daggers aside and removed the scroll.

"Hey, man, be gentle with that!" exclaimed Bruce.

"Get comfortable, Bindel. We're about to go back in history."

After Joel placed the scroll in front of them on two pieces of broken rock, they unrolled the first section. Joel began to read. As he was an expert in Egyptology, the material presented no problem. In fact it was like reading simple English.

A Timely Scenario

I am Amenemseth, scribe and storyteller, serving my Pharoah Amenhotep. One day in the city of Akhetaton Nor, a baby was born to the Princess Nefermanto. The baby was wizened, old looking, and seemed ill.

DR. HYFORCEPSAKON

PRINCESS
NEFERMANTO

Rather than be chastised for producing an abnormal child, the princess asked her servant, Enos, to dispose of the baby. However, Enos, who had no children of her own, could not do this and decided to place the baby in a straw basket and then put it in a nearby stream. She placed the crying infant in the basket, hastily wrote a few words on a sheet of papyrus detailing the account of his birth and his Tut score, and watched as the current quickly swept the basket away.

Several miles downstream, a woman named Iottacare was doing her wash. "Boy, have I had a day," she mused. "One baby-protective development (BPD) case after another. And then those little twins, Romulus and Remus, were born. I wonder…" She looked up almost as the basket was upon her.

"What's this?" She reached over and snatched the basket, pulling it to her side. "Oh, no, a baby abandoned in the bulrushes. He looks healthy

enough. I wonder what his Tut score was. Oh, this scroll may tell me something."

Iottacare read on and learned that the pregnancy was normal until the last two months when Princess Nefermanto had stopped eating. Her obstetrician, Dr. Hyforcepsakon, had tried to convince her that nourishment was necessary for the growing infant within her body, but she would not listen. The baby was born at eight months, scrawny but feisty.

Dr. Hyforcepsakon had given the infant a Tut score of VII and IX. It is interesting to note that a servant nurse in attendance scored IV and V, at one and five minutes respectively.

THE TUT SCORE IS Ⅶ & Ⅸ

Iottacare examined the infant and noted a thin baby with a furrowed brow and a worried expression on his face. Pulses were good, and as she placed her ear on his chest, she heard good, strong heart tones.

"This baby is doing extraordinarily well for such an experience," she said. "But he needs to be admitted to our ASBU (Akenhaton Sick Baby Unit)."

Iottacare picked up the ram's horn that she always carried and blew several short blasts. Kee-aw, kee-aw, kee-kee kee-kee, kee-aw—it sounded like a bleating goat. She repeated this procedure three times, and then she waited. A few minutes later, she heard the faint return signal.

"Good," she said. "The Babylon Transport Team should soon be here. In the meantime I will keep the baby warm."

A few minutes later, the Babylon Transport Team pulled up to the shore.

"Hello, Iottacare," said Ualine, the transport fellow. "What's up?"

"Boy, have I had a day in the Fertile Crescent. This abandoned baby has a Tut score that is either good or bad, depending upon who you believe. It looks like an SFD baby."

"Iotta, what is SFD?"

"I'm sorry, I know we promised Akenhton that we would try not to use abbreviations. It means, 'small for dates.' I don't know why we are having all these small babies."

"I have heard that there are plagues about, and that down the road there were locusts, vermin, and pestilence. I read about this in the weekly Haggadah."

"UA, I hate to interrupt you, but this baby is getting cold and jittery. You'd better load him into the transporter and get him to Cairo-Practors Hospital. Make sure to rinse your hands. I think there is some Sphinxsohex in the transporter. UA, how long do you think it will take us to get the baby there?"

"With this new transporter, it won't take forty days and forty nights. You can be sure of that."

A concerned expression suddenly appeared on Iottacare's face. "UA, I just thought of something. What will we do about consent? I know you don't know the first A's and B's about these ethical issues, but we will need to stop at the palace and have the king sign a proclamation...and get Jehovah to witness it."

"Iotta, you are really into the social aspects of this case. Perhaps one day there will be a place for social—let's see what to call you people—yes, workers...social workers in the ASBU setting.   All you are ever interested in is the mother's relationship with her baby. I've heard more than enough about separation and breast-feeding. More nonsense, if you ask me."

"UA, that's not fair, and you know it. You know that we social workers, as you call us, are into bondage. I just don't want the baby separated from his mummy. What if...what if we can't find a home for the baby? What if the foster parents don't speak Mesopotamian? What if they can't pay for the care at Cairo-Practors Hospital and fork up the dough?"

"Dough? I thought matzoh was the up-and-coming thing these days."

"Now, that's premature. First let's get him to the hospital, then we will do the matzoh number. For now we still need dough."

"Iotta, why is this case different from all other cases?"

"Simple, UA, In all other cases, we admit the baby to the unit and then do teaching with the parents, but in this case, we need to instruct the home-care nursing servant. Are you almost ready to go?"

"Yes, Iotta. Do you want to ride with me or wait for your own chariot?"

"You go on ahead. Pedepodomen promised to pick me up when the sun-dial hits four o'clock."

"See you later, hon."

"OK, UA. Listen—tell Lottapush that I've named the baby Elmer. Tell her to try and boil some water with a chicken in it and feed the baby the broth. My grandmother, Sophie, says this is healthy."

"Should they add anything to the broth?"

"Funny you should ask, UA. I was fooling around in the kitchen today and rolled up some matzoh into little round ball. I found that it floated in the water. Perhaps this would add some extra nourishment and prevent the jitters. Try it—you'll like it."

"OK, Iotta. Give my regards to Pedepodomen. See you later."

Iotta watched the chariot pull away. "Boy, am I tired," she thought. "I'd walk a mile for a camel, but I really feel stressed. Perhaps I have the newly publicized Burning Bush Burn Out Syndrome. I think I'd better..."

Bruce stopped reading as the hieroglyphics became faded and almost incomprehensible.

"Joel, we'd best take the scrolls with us and decipher them in our laboratory."

"Fine with me," answered Bruce, "but I'm dying to know more about the story."

Later that night, after much work and two bottles of Aphora, the two men learned that Akhenaton didn't like the name Elmer and changed it to Moses.

The rest....is history.

Neonatal Workforce
(Summer 1988)

In February 1787, Philadelphia was the second-largest city in the English-speaking world. State delegates began to arrive in Philadelphia, filled with apprehension and hope as the leaders of the country met to attempt an almost impossible task. Men such as Madison, Franklin, Hamilton, and Jefferson—to name a few, were given the assignment to set up a workable relationship between central and state government. The ideal number of delegates required to fill the need of the population was also an agenda item for the conference. While the colonists waited, the leaders held a roundtable discussion.

A Timely Scenario

Two hundred years later, almost to the day, another roundtable took place, with delegates assigned an almost impossible task. The question asked was, "Are there too many neonatologists?" To best answer this question, they reviewed the history of neonatology. Topics discussed included: the number and distribution of neonatologists, pediatric manpower projections, regionalization and deregionalization of perinatal care, the relationship between primary, secondary, and tertiary centers, and finally the interorganizational conflicts that accompany all of these topics.

FEBRUARY 1987

One of the delegates pointed out that ten years earlier (February 1977) there was a need for 1,634 neonatologists with the anticipated number of 512 being "board certified." These figures were derived from the numbers of neonatal units, the number of patients per neonatologist, the average daily census, the average number of patient days, attrition and burnout, section of town, and the availability of a good delicatessen nearby for snacks.

Several years later another committee met to estimate the need for neonatologists. Armed with changing care patterns and the increased number of very low-birth-weight infants, they decided that 1,479 neonatologists was the correct figure.

During the three days of the 1987 meeting, the delegates presented material related to specific and general needs. They discussed different models, and data showed that by the end of 1987 there would be at least 2,000 board certified neonatologists and certainly many more pediatricians practicing neonatology without board certification. It was a wonderful three days spent in the sunshine of Arizona, with good food, intellectual stimulation, and serious discussion. Although a statistician was not present, it was clear that there would be no simple way to define all the variables in order to come up with a number to satisfy all those present.

After reviewing the material from this conference and the meetings held earlier, I believe a simple solution is at hand. A relationship exists between the number of neonatal abstracts presented at the American Pediatric Society/Society for Pediatric Research Academic meeting and the number of neonatologists required. The number of neonatal abstracts presented, multiplied by two, will fulfill the need and answer the question.

1986—626 abstracts; neonatologists needed—1,352
1987—721 abstracts; neonatologists needed—1,442
1988—789 abstracts; neonatologists needed—1,578

This seems to be a more simple method, and the expense of further conference time might be avoided if this concept was adapted. The question of the need for a nearby delicatessen is still under consideration.

Submitted by Perinate
Bitcoins: A New Reimbursement Model

Recently, a group of men gathered in Union Square to buy and sell bitcoins. A bitcoin is an experimental, decentralized, digital currency with no central authority and enables instant payments to anyone, anywhere in the world. The concept of the bitcoin is one of crypto-currency. It builds upon the notion that money is any object or any sort of record accepted as payment for goods, services and repayments of debt in a given country or socio-economic context.

The supply of bitcoins is regulated by software and cannot be manipulated by any government, bank, organization or individual.

What is all of this gobblygook? Is this real world economics and business? Perhaps, physicians should seek reimbursement in bitcoins since the transactions are fast and cost very little compared with other payment networks

New York Times - May 6, 2013

Hope in Forayes
(Winter 1988)

January 16, 1988

To: The Editor
The Journal of Perinatology
1040 B. St. Suite 209
San Rafael, CA 94901

Dear Editor:

Enclosed, find a manuscript entitled "The Use of 2-3-4 Dinitrophenyloxymatrix in the Treatment of the Very Low-Birth-Weight Infant Placed in an Intermediate-Care Intensive-Care Unit Near a Rural Area in the Southwestern United States."

I wrote this article because I felt readers of the *Journal of Perinatology* would be interested in such a subject.

I hope your editorial board will act favorably after reading this material, for my tenure as an instructor in Neonatal Epidemiology may depend upon it. My son Richard will probably not be able to get new shoes if this manuscript is not accepted.

In consideration of the *Journal of Perinatology*'s taking action in reviewing and editing my submission, I hereby transfer, assign, or otherwise convey all copyright ownership to the California Perinatal Association in the event that such work is published by the *Journal of Perinatology*.

Hoping in advance for a positive response. My wife Patricia and my mom Beatrice say, "Hi."

Sincerely yours,
Hope In Forayes, MD

Answer to Dr. Forayes (Choose the Appropriate Response)

Number 1

February 20, 1988

To: Hope in Forayes, MD
Instructor, Neonatal Epidemiology
The Hospital of the Fair Samaritan
223-4445-1314 SW North St.
Belvedere, AR 71901

Dear Dr. Forayes:
    Thank you for submitting your manuscript to the *Journal of Perinatology*. The editorial board currently is reviewing your manuscript. We will notify you as soon as this process is complete.
    I appreciate your interest in the *Journal of Perinatology*.

Sincerely,
The Perinate

Number 2

February 20, 1988

To: Hope in Forayes, MD
Instructor, Neonatal Epidemiology
The Hospital of the Fair Samaritan
223-4445-1314 SW North St.
Belvedere, AR 71901

Dear Dr. Forayes:
    Thank you for submitting your manuscript to the *Journal of Perinatology*. The editorial board currently is reviewing your manuscript. We will notify you as soon as this process is complete.

I appreciate your interest in the *Journal of Perinatology*. Send my regards to Patricia and Beatrice. Have you looked at any low-cost shoe outlets?

Sincerely,
The Perinate

Number 3

February 20, 1988

To: Hope in Forayes, MD
Instructor, Neonatal Epidemiology
The Hospital of the Fair Samaritan
223-4445-1314 SW North St.
Belvedere, AR 71901

Dear Dr. Forayes:
Thank you for submitting your manuscript to the *Journal of Perinatology*. Under normal circumstances the editorial board would review the manuscript. However, the title of your submission, "The Use of 2-3-4 Dinitrophenyloxymatrix in the Treatment of the Very Low-Birth-Weight Infant Placed in an Intermediate-Care Intensive-Care Unit Near a Rural Area in the Southwestern United States" is longer than the entire abstract.

Therefore please revise the title before we consider reviewing the rest of the manuscript.

Enclosed, find $11.99, with which you can purchase shoes for Richard.

Sincerely,
The Perinate

HOPE IN FORAYES

Signing Bonuses for Nurses
(June 1989)

A dry bagel and an empty NutraSweet packet for his coffee was not the way to begin any morning. The brown liquid in the teeth marks at the lip of the styrofoam cup reminded Richard of the foul taste.

Richard Whiting, chief arbitrator for the perinatal-neonatal section of Grandview Memorial Hospital, had a busy day ahead. Negotiations among several of the nurses, social workers, and respiratory therapists had been nonstop for the past week, and for those not signing new contracts, arbitration was the only answer.

The first file seemed interesting. Liza Rosenfeld, RN, was a neonatal nurse with ten years of experience. This time she was seeking a bonus for signing, plus an increased salary for her 1988 statistics.

What have we here? Richard said to himself.

Her 330 THSE (twelve-hour shift equivalents), thirty days of vacation, and four days of sick leave were pretty impressive. She had an SIV ratio (successful IV attempts, expressed as a percentage) of 81 %, up from 68 % in 1987. Her RAP (radial arterial puncture) percentage also had improved over the earlier time period. Her DDT (double-duty time) and ETU (endotracheal intubations) were somewhat down, but her PODA (physicians' orders deciphering ability) was her forte. Liza was asking not only for an 11 % pay increase and a bonus but also long-term deferments and real estate provisions.

A real tough one, thought Richard. *I hope she signs.* "Rita, bring me the Skelley file, will you?" he called to his secretary.

"Look on your desk near the fish food. I left it there this morning," she answered.

Pushing away journal articles, contracts, and red-and-yellow goldfish flakes, he found the file.

Pat Skelley, RN, perinatal nurse, was said to be the best FMSI (fetal-monitoring-strip interpreter) in the department. The notes in the file revealed that her CDDA (cervical-dilation diagnostic ability) was 0.8cm ± .3, a high score. Her CCSOT (crash-cesarean-section organizing time) was under twenty minutes (the average in her age group was twenty-five minutes), and she was popular with physicians and other personnel.

Pat was not only seeking a bonus for signing but also wanted a clause in her contract specifying added funds for services in case of a management lockout. She wanted a three-year contract with a two-year option.

I hope the directors of nursing, perinatology, and neonatology back me on this one, Richard thought. *I might have to rule in her favor, which would set a precedent.*

"Dr. Whiting, call for you on 81," said Rita. "It's Ron Finer."

"Good morning, Ron. I hope you have good news for me about the Rosenfeld case."

"You've lucked out again, Richard. She signed a few moments ago and even gave up the real estate options. I've also heard that the Skelley nurse is close to signing as well. We're trying to convince her that a two-year contract with outreach appearances at other hospitals would be better than a three-year, all-inclusive agreement. I'll know if we've signed her within the hour. If not, get ready for a fight. Her lawyer and agent won't settle for a simple contract."

"Thanks, Ron. Please keep me posted."

Richard picked up a new file and began reading. Dave Born, RRT, refused to talk to anyone except the arbitrator. His strengths included a fast SURT (setting-up respirator time) and a respectable BGAWART (blood-gas analysis within a reasonable time) score. But he didn't change respiratory tubings often enough and disliked transports.

I'd like this case to come to my personal attention, thought Richard. *Dave Born would never get a bonus for signing.*

Richard read on…and on…

Submitted by Perinate

Medical Billing: Price Controls?

Medical billing practices are again being questioned as the price of medical care escalates. Medicare has provided data revealing disparate prices throughout the country. For example, the average hospital charge for a knee and hip replacement varied from $ 32,000 to $ 223,000 in a local catchment area. The "secrets of medical pricing are closely guarded" and these divergent practices are arbitrary and dysfunctional. Healthcare professional charges are a fraction of hospital charges but are just as complicated.

I charge this, you pay that, who decides the rules?

In the scheme of bill and pay, the docs appear as fools.

The Apgar Score
(September 1989)

Virginia Apgar, in '53,
was practicing anesthesiology.
She said to colleagues with great frustration,
"The newborn babe needs observation.
Correct assessment, with more attention,
leads to appropriate intervention.
If we pick numbers that seem to jive,
can this predict who will survive?"
A scale devised that very year,
was clinically oriented and did seem fair.
Heart rate, reflex irritability, and muscle tone,
were numbered singly, each one alone.
Respiratory effort and color too,
hence the score—but what to do?
Measured at minutes, one, five, and ten,
Instructed what to do and when.
Problems arose with such a roar,
who should assign this Apgar score?
The obstetrician called numbers high,
for perfect babies would not die.
The pediatrician, not wanting blame,
called numbers low, which was a shame.
This left the task to the poor nurse,
who often found the job a curse.
Five clinical signs made up the score,
but in reality there were several more.

A Timely Scenario

The obstetricians yelled and booed,
wailing that they'd soon be sued.
Pediatricians countered, "Don't be afraid.
'Asphyxia' is a term that soon will fade."
And then some babies born premature,
could not be measured with the score.
Cord pH and gestational age,
made the number a poor gauge.
Faulty recall and postdated noting,
had the lawyers really gloating.
Potential help for this condition,
mimics Olympic competition.
Skaters, gymnasts, and divers too,
are all assigned a score by few.
A special team of five or more,
could redefine the Apgar score.
In house, on call for deliveries,
their Apgar scores would surely please.
A 3, or 4 , or 7.1,
hold up your cards—we've just begun.

The Apgar Score

Three and one half million births a year,
who will fund a cost so dear?
Perhaps the answer is soporific,
as we attempt to be scientific.
Encourage closer observation,
adapt a score without inflation.
Modify existing terms,
we've opened up a can of worms.
So Virginia Apgar in 53,
really predicted what would be.
She walked the walk, and lit the lamp,
the honor was a postage stamp.

Submitted by Perinate
Student Debt: Lawyers and Doctors

In 2004 applications to law schools numbered about 100,000. Today that number is decreased to about 54,000. Average annual tuition for law school has increased from about $23,000 in 2001 to over $ 40,000 in 2012. In addition, law school debt is also increased even though law school is only a three year commitment. Jobs are scarce. However, the complex legislation dealing with the new healthcare proposals require knowledgeable attorneys to decipher the legalese.

The numbers for medical school fees and accumulated debt are even higher. In order to become specialized, further training and henceforth debt is additional. Perhaps there needs to be consideration of "fellowships" in law sub-specialties which would provide an improved framework for their practice, resulting in better advice to clients.

Hamlet II—
The Cocaine-Addicted Infant
(September 1990)

Hamlet II is now eight weeks old. Unknown to his father, Hamlet I, his mother, Ophelia, used cocaine during her pregnancy and continues her habit, even though she is breast-feeding. The infant had irritability and jitteriness after birth and now shows signs of poor feeding and neurobehavioral abnormalities. Hamlet I has just received the report of a positive cocaine immunoassay screen on Ophelia.

A Timely Scenario

Hamlet hangs up the phone. He is alone in their two-bedroom condominium. The hazy sunshine filters through the vertical blinds. He turns and looks outside, squinting.

Ham. O, that this too too solid flesh would melt,
Thaw and resolve itself into a dew!
Or that the Everlasting had not fix'd
His canon 'gainst self-slaughter! O God! God!
How weary, stale, flat, and unprofitable
Seem to me all the uses of this world!
Fie on't! ah, fie! 'tis an unweeded garden,
Filled with cannabis and coca leaves.
That grows to seed; things rank and gross in nature
Possess it merely. That it should come to this!
But two months born, small in size, irritable.
Lack of bonding thought to be colic.
Heaven and earth!
Must I remember? He would hang on her,
As if increase of appetite had grown
By what it fed on; and yet, through her milk,
Poor growth, fits of crying—
Let me not think on't.
Parens patriae [the stage as parent]
Superseded *Roe vs. Wade.*
Jurisdiction, constitutional protection…
Child abuse—is there a legality
for protection of the fetus from socially unacceptable
and dangerous maternal abuse?
…..Frailty, thy name is addiction!

—*Hamlet II, Act 2, Scene 1*

Editorial—Nothing Ventured, Nothing Gained
(December 1991)

The health industry in the United States is a mess. Access to care, cost of care, and effectiveness of care always have been debatable issues. Now, however, rationing of health care due to the shrinking dollar has become a reality. Many solutions have been offered as the health dollar assumes a greater portion of the gross national product. Most believe that some form of national health insurance is on the horizon, but should we follow the Canadian, British, or German model?

Once again, the health-care industry should look to the business community for an answer. When competition increases and profits decrease, the business community identifies potential customers and attempts to get their business. When a company's stock price is low, the officers sometimes increase their own stock holdings. These purchases of stock are of public record and typically signify confidence in the company. No mention of kickbacks here. It is not considered a moral or legal sin to invest in your own company. It is just good business.

Ah, if it were only so simple for the medical profession! Sending patients to a laboratory where one has an interest is considered fraud. "Overutilization for profit!" screams the legislature. No longer can a pharmaceutical company take a physician or nurse out to lunch without a question of a kickback emerging. No more free pens available. Soon the sticky pads will disappear as well. What are we to do?

A Timely Scenario

There are certainly those in all professions who will send patients, clients or customers to their own facility or store, simply to make money. Most of us, however, have entered our profession with the goal of being honest and helpful, and we attempt to provide the best service. If another laboratory can do the test at a lower price with the same quality and efficiency, the professional investor should demand that the price to the patient be lowered. Quality must always remain the gold standard.

"What has this to do with perinatology?" you might ask. Although this introduction may appear long, it sets the stage for my concept of join-venturing perinatal services. The system follows simple, basic business principles. First, determine expenses for all perinatal services. The hospital can provide meticulous information about costs. Then, determine payments for these services from insurance companies, government, and private payors. If the balance sheet reveals profitability, the next step is easy. If it does not, a determination must be made as to how to cut costs, increase efficiency, or increase volume. Once profitability is realized, sell shares in this "perinatal system." Physicians, nurses, respiratory therapists, hospital employees, and even nonhospital personnel can invest.

The shares should be low enough to ensure a broad base for the entire community. Most important, the individual working in the system will have an added incentive to provide the highest degree of service and increase volume and efficiency. The employee is no longer just an employee but, as a part owner, assumes a different responsibility. Hospitals today are marketing their services to any group that will listen. What is different about the concept of marketing a perinatal joint venture? It is true that there are now legislative concerns about medical professionals investing in their own businesses. It is interesting that no other profession that practices "good business sense" is held to such standards. These obstacles still can be overcome by careful joint-venture design so that all legal requirements are met. It might be wiser to remove all legal entanglements and allow quality, supply, and demand to determine economic success, and weed out the dishonest individuals.

I want the nurse, respiratory therapist, social worker, and even the person in central supply to be my partner. If in today's environment we must function as businesspersons, then let us do it!

The worst thing we can do is to sit back and let regulations obstruct our basic rights, both economically and intellectually. It is time to swim against the current and joint-venture together.

Submitted by Perinate
All You Need is Love

We counsel our medical students to understand that in the practice of medicine today, the student must "love" what he/she is doing. What is the real meaning of love? According to Lily Tomlin, "if love is the answer, can you rephrase the question?" Love means nothing in tennis but is everything in life. Lucy in the Peanuts comic strip sums it up best by saying, "all I really need is love, but a little chocolate now and then doesn't hurt".

As our trainees progress from students to doctors there will be many times where they will not love what they are doing. When an obstacle occurs, if the student really loves what they are doing, this love of medicine, like a river will cut a new path. However, an additional piece of chocolate would seal the deal.

Changes in Perinatal Health Care over the Centuries
(March 1992)

The Los Angeles Times, January 25, 2006
The president, in her State of the Union address, discussed the crisis in perinatal health care in many areas of the United States. A select panel was organized early in 2005 to study the problem and suggest solutions. The following is the first of a three-part series dealing with perinatal health- care issues.

The History of Obstetrical Care

The word "*obstetrics*" is derived from the Latin term "*obstetrix*," which means "midwife." It also is related to the Latin word "*obstare,*" which means "to stand by" or "to stand in front of." There is some controversy, however, as some etymologists believe the original word was "*adstetrix,*" which mean "woman assisting" (the parturient). The term "*midwife*" was used as early as 1303. It is derived from the Middle English "*mid,*" meaning "with," and "*wif,*" in the sense of "woman." The modern use of the word "*obstetrics*" appeared for the first time in 1819. The following narrative detailing the history of obstetrical care through the ages will foster understanding regarding the present crisis in perinatal health care.

30,000 BC: Gambles Care (Africa)
Cave Wall Figures

The woman Cleona, attended by the woman Renie, gave birth to a male child. After resting for a period of time and suckling the child, she left the cave to gather wood and berries. Renie was given two chicken wings for her assistance.

30,000 YEARS BC, GAMBLES CARE (AFRICA)

3,000 BC: Saqqarah, Egypt
Clay Tablets

Allantep, grand vizier to King Roytze of Egypt, supervised the delivery of Cleona, wife of Anthony. The slave Renie delivered the male child. After resting for a period of time and suckling the child, she rose, dressed, and prepared dinner. Allantep received a glass vase for his services. Renie received a finely woven shawl.

164 AD, Rome
Papyrus Scroll

Jacobaides, physician partner of Galen, attended the delivery of the woman, Cleona. The attendant, Renie, used massage and poultices to alleviate Cleona's pain before delivery. Renie delivered a male child. After suckling the child, Renie rested for the next two days. Jacobaides charged a month's supply of oil for his services. Renie received two bronze goblets.

1200: Bologna, Italy
Bound, Printed Material

Physician Shell de Singerini, with the help of his assistant, Renie, delivered the baby of Cleona de Luzzi. The male child was born with the cord around his neck but suffered no ill effects. As Count de Luzzi was a friend of the family, Dr. de Singerini accepted no payment. Renie declined payment but accepted a small gold spoon as a gift. Cleona suckled the child immediately after birth and remained at bed rest for six days.

1303: London, England
Printed Midwife's Journal

Mrs. Cleona Spenser gave birth to a male child on Saturday, June 3, 1303. The midwife, Renie, delivered the child. Dr. Roger Phelan was in attendance. Dr. Phelan charged a half pound for his services. Renie received a half guinea. Mrs. Spenser breast-fed the child and regained her strength over the next two weeks.

1303, LONDON, ENGLAND

MRS. CLEONA SPENSER

RENIE

½ GUINEA

1833: Berlin, Germany
Physician's Diary

Clarkes Muller, Professor of Geburtshilfe, delivered a male child on June 3, 1833. The mother, Mrs. Cleona Gerlitzke, did not ask for pain medication. Although Renie Reiff was available, Dr. Muller wanted no assistance and finished the delivery in two hours. He charged three hundred marks for his services. Mrs. Gerlitzke breast-fed the child and then slept for the next eighteen hours.

1833, BERLIN, GERMANY

MRS. CLEONA GERLITZKE

PROFESSOR MULLER

300 MARKS

1905: Kranzberg, South Dakota
Physician's Office Records

Dr. Robert Kranz performed the delivery of a male child on Mrs. Cleona Spartz, at her farm in Kranzberg on June 3, 1905. Renie Zaug who would have normally assisted was out milking the cows and missed the delivery. Dr. Kranz received three dollars and a side of beef for his services. Mrs. Spartz breast-fed the child and rested for three days before returning to her duties on the farm.

1905, KRANZBERG, SOUTH DAKOTA

CLEONA SPARTZ

DR. KRANZ

1945: Brooklyn, New York
Hospital Chart Records

Dr. Charles Glassman, staff obstetrician, delivered a pair of identical twins at Brookdale Hospital on February 16, 1945. The mother, Mrs. Cleona Finken, was attended by several nurses. Renie was the obstetrical nursing supervisor. Dr. Glassman declined payment, as Mrs. Finken was his niece. However, in honor of his generosity, one of the twins was named Charles. Renie was paid by the hospital. Mrs. Finken used Carnation milk to feed the infants and remained in the hospital for six days. The hospital bill was $106.

1945, BROOKLYN, NEW YORK

MRS. CLEONA FINKEN

DR. GLASSMAN

1972: Kalamazoo, Michigan
Physician's Records and Hospital Records

Mrs. Cleona Bowen delivered a male infant on Saturday, June 3, 1972. Her obstetrician, Dr. Jay Hartline, performed the delivery under spinal anesthesia. The baby's Apgar scores were 8/9 at 1 and 5 minutes respectively. Mrs. Bowen chose a regular formula for the infant, as she would have to return to work in three months. Mrs. Bowen's hospital insurance paid 80% of her physician and hospital charges. Mrs. Bowen did not have any deductible on her policy. She remained in the hospital for five days. The obstetrician's bill was $385. The hospital bill was $468. When she left she gave her favorite nurse, Renie, a box of See's candy.

A Timely Scenario

1986: Boston, Massachusetts
Physician's Records and Hospital Records

Mrs. Cleona Arnold gave birth to a male infant on Saturday, June 3, 1986. Her obstetrician, Dr. Ruth Fritzhand, used an epidural for analgesia. The baby's Apgar scores were 8/9 at 1 and 5 minutes respectively. Mrs. Arnold chose a soybean formula, as there was a history of milk allergy in the family, and she would have to return to work in six weeks. Mrs. Arnold's insurance paid 70% of the entire bill, with a $250 deductible. She was only allowed to spend three days in the hospital. The obstetrician's bill was $640. The hospital bill was $1,100. The obstetrical nurse, Renie, assisted the family to the car. Mrs. Arnold gave her a kiss and a yellow rose.

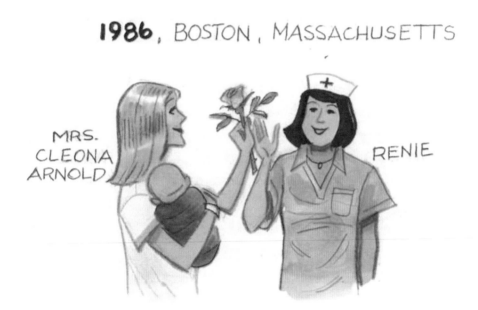

1991: Los Angeles, California
Physician's Records, Hospital Records, and Quality Assurance Committee Records

A male infant was born to Mrs. Cleona Berkman on June 3, 1991. Her obstetrician, Hal Tang, gave the infant an Apgar score of 8/9 at one and five minutes respectively. Nurse Renie scored the child a 6/7. No analgesia was used, as Mr. and Mrs. Berkman used the Lamaze technique. Her HMO insurance allowed for a one-day hospital stay. Her capitated insurance plan charged her $6 per month. The hospital was paid on a per diem basis. Mrs. Berkman breast-fed the infant and returned to work in three weeks.

1991, LOS ANGELES, CALIFORNIA

MRS. CLEONA BERKMAN

NURSE RENIE

6/7

1992: San Diego, California
Physician's Records, Hospital Records, Quality Assurance Committee Records, and Hospital Attorney's Records

Ms. Cleona Babin gave birth to a male infant on June 3, 1992. Dr. Mannino Coen administered a continuous caudal for analgesia. He gave the baby an Apgar score of 8/9 at one and five minutes. Perinatal nurse Renie scored the child a 6/7. Ms. Babin had no prenatal care and had presented to the emergency department earlier that day. A drug screen was positive for cocaine. Although transfer was attempted, no other hospital would accept her as a patient. She remained in the hospital for six hours and was discharged, to be followed up at the county clinic. The baby used standard rotational hospital formula. Ms. Babin would provide no information about her future plans.

1996: Pittsburgh, Pennsylvania
Physician's Diary

Mrs. Cleona Bertolin gave birth to a male infant at her home on Cedar Street on June 3, 1996. Dr. Clark Feldburch, assisted by his nurse, Renie, delivered the baby. Apgar scores were not recorded. Mrs. Bertolin breast-fed the baby and was allowed to rest for three days before returning to work as a computer repairwoman. Dr. Feldburch received $450 for the delivery. Nurse Renie received a pink mohair sweater.

1996, PITTSBURGH, PENNSYLVANIA

MRS. CLEONA BERTOLIN

RENIE

A Timely Scenario

1997: San Jose, California
Physician's Notes

On June 3, 1997, Mrs. Cleona Sprague gave birth to a male infant. Midwife Renie actually delivered the baby but was supervised by Dr. Vern Bach. Mrs. Sprague breast-fed the infant and rested for two days before returning to work as a checker at a nearby supermarket. The midwife charged $250 for the delivery. Dr. Vern Bach received a pair of wool gloves.

2001: Manhattan, New York
Taped Recording

Ms. Cleona Furman delivered a male infant on June 3, 2001. The weight of the baby was not recorded. A friend, Renie, helped to deliver the infant. Ms. Furman breast-fed the infant, slept for a few hours, and then needed to return to work as a motor woman for the transit authority. As payment to Renie, she promised to babysit for her on weekends.

Obstetrical care has now come full circle

Submitted by Perinate
The Appetizer Before the Entree

Have you ever gone into a bakery where there are samples of pastries enticing one to taste the goods before deciding on what to buy? New products and devices are marketed to physicians. The success of these products and/or devices oftentimes depends on the approach offered by the pharmaceutical representative. We have gone to dinners, conferences, CME courses with the "cover" of education as the benefit. At times the rewards are "over the top". A week in Tahiti, all expenses paid to learn about a new drug could raise some eyebrows. The financial relationships with industry to doctors and hospitals will be scrutinized even further when the federal Physician Payment Sunshine Act goes into effect. Do these incentives generate positive behavior? Do physicians still make decisions that are in the best interests of their patients?

I believe that my sampling a piece of pastry was certainly not too lavish. Are the principles the same or is the type and amount of incentive the critical issue?

Roni Caryn Rabin. Light on Doctors' Lucrative Industry Ties. New York Times 5/14/2013

Health-Care Reform
(May/June 1993)

I've been around for many years,
and always think it funny,
that issues like "health-care reform,"
arise when there's no money.

I've dealt with DRGs with ease,
with Medi-Cal and Caid,
but this administration's plan,
does make me afraid.

I wrote to Ira Magaziner,
in words that were not coarse,
asking him if I could join,
Hill's own "Health-Care Task Force."

After all I've worked so hard
in perinatal care,
with issues such as reimbursement,
I know I would be fair.

I'm uncomfortable with "health alliances,"
this term to me seems hard,
and yet they plan to give us all
a "health security card."

A Timely Scenario

Basic care for everyone,
with "managed competition,"
do you think the plan will work?
will it come to fruition?

Hillary won't take my calls,
or recognize my faxes,
and yet I know she won't forget,
to raise my income taxes.

Provide incentives, strike a balance,
test the people's muster,
who can blame the legislators.,
for their filibuster?

Price ceilings failed—can you remember?
The president's no martyr.
Roosevelt cried, Dick Nixon lied,
and left it all to Carter.

Rationed care in Oregon,
discards the "tiny weight,"
leaving us in such a quandary,
should we resuscitate?

The health-care board seems so biased,
is there a doc or nurse?
Statements issued are not friendly,
to me they seem too terse.

We don't need administrators,
or middle management.
All these people, wasted money,—
it won't save a cent.

Instead involve staff perinatal,
to tocolyse the scene.
We will offer terms per diem,
and make the charge serene.

I do believe it's time for change,
and health care will get better.
But please involve the Perinate
and his gal, Perinetta.

Editorial—Then and Now: Resuscitation...Who to Train?
(2000)

Over the years I have pointed out in many of these columns that to understand the present and plan for the future, we must appreciate the past. William Silverman, MD, wrote a wonderful book that should be required reading for all personnel caring for mothers and newborns. This treatise, titled *Where's the Evidence?*, was published by Oxford University Press in 1998 and is a series of essays, written in the past, with commentaries on what has transpired over the ensuing years. I've taken the liberty of using this approach to present a topic that was offered to our readers in 1984, along with subsequent developments over the past fifteen years.

1984—Resuscitation at Birth...Who to Train?

Traditionally pediatric residents are trained to resuscitate newborn infants in the delivery room. Over a period of time, most become proficient at this task. Indeed the ability to intubate is required for true admission into the fraternity or sorority of "physicianhood." Yet the ability to resuscitate, including intubation when necessary, does not require an MD degree, or any other degree for that matter. It does require theoretical and practical training and regular application of the skills acquired to remain proficient.

A Timely Scenario

Once the average pediatric resident graduates and becomes an attending, opportunities to practice and maintain these acquired skills decrease precipitously. Many pediatric residents report that the need to intubate an infant at birth occurs only once or twice a year after their graduation from pediatric training, a year in which a disproportionate percentage of their patients are newborns. The years that follow generally provide even less exposure, thereby permitting further deterioration of their resuscitation skills. From time to time, refresher courses are provided with mannequin or cat models. Nonetheless the true expert is the person who practices his or her art regularly. Cardiac surgeons who perform only two or three coronary-artery bypass grafts per year, or general surgeons who perform only two or three cholecystectomies per year, or cardiologists who perform only two or three cardiac catherizations per year will not be granted hospital privileges or will have their privileges revoked. Why should the difficult task of expert neonatal resuscitation be viewed any differently?

If pediatric residents are the wrong group to train, which is the right group? Many, if not most, infants who require resuscitation in the delivery room require it unexpectedly. Therefore every delivery service should have a designated resuscitator available in the proximity of the delivery room area twenty-four hours a day.

A delivery room nurse would fill this role most easily, although other disciplines such as respiratory care may be adequate. Sufficient numbers of nurses need to be trained to provide one nurse resuscitator on each and every shift. Trained personnel should be limited in number so as not to dilute the available experience. Even relatively small delivery services may have enough infants requiring resuscitation to allow each trained nurse several opportunities per month to practice and maintain his or her skills. Physicians would then be deprived of the glory, but birth asphyxia would be able to take a holiday more often.

2000 Resuscitation at Birth...Who to Train?

The ideas noted in this 1984 editorial were certainly predictive of what has developed today. There are many reasons for these changes, and in certain areas, we are not yet where we should be. The entire pediatric-residency experience in the neonatal intensive-care unit (NICU) has been shortened considerably. Under current standards, a resident spends three months in the NICU; therefore he or she has fewer opportunities to perform intubations. In the past, senior residents were the first to arrive in the delivery room for a resuscitation. Now, other members of the "team" are more proficient. Upon their graduation to practice, their experience has been dampened considerably. Once they are in practice, several scenarios take place. With many managed-care practices, pediatricians are encouraged to see patients in their offices and to spend as little time as possible taking care of patients in the hospital. Thus, "hospitalists' or "neonatologists" have assumed this responsibility. Most obstetricians would prefer that there be a designated neonatologist available to the delivery room at all times. In hospitals in which the neonatologist "sleeps in," this is possible. Most hospitals delivering babies, however, do not have this capability. Therefore the presence of the neonatologist may not be an option.

Other personnel must be trained. In the ideal situation, nurses are the obvious choice. Except for tertiary hospitals, however, the personnel required and the number of "intubating experiences" would not be adequate. Second, to assign a nurse to this role who is already taking care of two or three other infants would be difficult. Third, in tertiary centers, which nurse would go on transports if necessary? Neonatal nurse practitioners would be perfect in this role, but they are usually part of the more specialized NICU team. Therefore, in many situations, the respiratory therapist has assumed the role of "intubator." Even primary hospitals today have respiratory therapists in house, and all hospitals with a delivery service need to have this as a policy.

Because, in medicine, we strive for the "ideal," what would this concept mean? A neonatal resuscitation team should be available for all deliveries. This team should be in house, and there needs to be a back up group if the team is called for a transport. This team should consist of at least a nurse and a respiratory therapist skilled in neonatal resuscitation, with a neonatologist available as a backup.

The American Academy of Pediatrics and the American Heart Association made our task easier with the creation of the Neonatal Resuscitation Program. The fourth edition of the Neonatal Resuscitation Program manual is forthcoming (the sixth edition was published in 2011). This program has become the most widely used course of the American Academy of Pediatrics around the world. Demonstrating proficiency in neonatal resuscitation must be required for physicians, nurses, and respiratory therapists working in hospitals that deliver babies.

We must realize that the number of times that resuscitation is necessary will not decrease. As larger numbers of very low-birth-weight infants are born, the number of resuscitations will increase. If we agree that the opportunities are there, and that the dedication and expertise are present, what is the dilemma?

THE NEONATAL RESUSCITATION TEAM

Cost, Cost, Cost!!!!!!

It takes money to pay for the training and the hiring of the personnel required to perform these duties. Hospitals are having a difficult time in this era of managed care, and we are not able to secure funding. Reimbursement for attending deliveries and performing resuscitation is poor at best, and the neonatologist cannot be in all places at once and might prefer that another group assume this role. The obstetrician and the anesthesiologist in the delivery room or surgical suite would much prefer that a pediatrician/neonatologist be present for the delivery. They know that, as physicians, they have the ultimate responsibility. The payers (both private and government) must adjust their goals accordingly to allow for improvement in this most critical aspect of newborn care. No one would argue that the first few minutes of life can determine the productivity of the individual for the future.

The editorial I wrote in 1984 was predictive of our current state in many ways but did not consider the fiscal consequences. I look forward to writing another editorial in 2015 on the same subject to determine whether or not we have become progressive and proactive or have simply eliminated the problem.

Post Script 2014

It is interesting that Virginia Apgar's goal in her early papers (1953) emphasized the need for an advocate for the baby after delivery. Now, sixty plus years later, we are suggesting the same concept. Lessons and advice from the past often have predictions for the future.

Submitted by Perinate
The Lowly Apostrophe

Do you know that there is a Domestic Names Committee of the United States Board on Geographic Names (founded in 1890)? This committee does not like apostrophes. Is Pikes Peak named for a Pike or Pikes? There is also a Apostrophe Protection Society whose function is to rally against the US apostrophe-eradication policy (who knew of such a policy?). Have you noticed that apostrophes are not welcome in the internet? McDonald's appears on the restaurant logo but on the internet it is listed as mcdonalds.com. The apostrophe was introduced into the English language in 1529 and its use has progressed and changed over time. In our neonatal nomenclature, we have separated the apostrophe's possessive nature. That is, although Down's report on classification of congenital idiots appeared in 1866. We describe these patients with Down Syndrome, not Down's Syndrome. The same is true for other syndromes described in the literature.

To Be Or Not To Be
Apos Tro Phe
That is The Question

Wall Street Journal - May 16, 2013

Editorial—Trickle, Trickle...
All Fall Down
(2000)

"Trickle economics" is a familiar term to most Americans. Alan Greenspan, Chairman of the Federal Reserve, and his board lower and raise interest rates, depending on the state of the economy. If inflation is a possibility, interest rate are increased, which will have an effect on all sectors and filter down to large corporations and finally the consumer, who will purchase less and therefore slow down an overexpanding economy. Laissez-Faire Economics 101—it all seems simple enough.

This trickle-economic approach, however, has now pervaded medicine and has changed the way physicians think and practice. I am tired this morning. I wish this malaise was due to the "happy exhaustion" physicians feel after a night on call, where our presence made a difference or we learned something new and found intellectual stimulation.

No, I am tired because I am beginning to believe that in this state of "health economics," physicians and hospitals are fighting a losing battle. Follow along with this concept, if you will.

Academic departments, receiving less grant funding and decreased remuneration, are asking the bench research faculty to take clinical calls and care for patients. The financial reasons are clear, but the following has occurred. First, with less time to spend in the laboratory, less research occurs, and basic advances, which we have seen over previous decades, are starting to decline. Second, the individuals now caring for patients opted for research as their primary interest (not clinical medicine); therefore they may be unsuited for this new responsibility. Patient care will suffer. Last, the number of original nonclinical research articles submitted to peer-reviewed medical journals has decreased because of this trickle-down approach. There is simply not enough money to allow for the usual and customary natural order.

In several renowned journals, commentaries have discussed the fact that many clinical studies appearing in journals have in fact been funded by drug companies. As a result these studies may offer biased information. The research group most likely would prefer not to receive these funds from the drug companies. However, if there are no other sources available and if disclaimers are offered, isn't it better to be able to do the research than to abandon the project because of lack of funds?

This trickle-down approach has affected pediatrics and neonatology with dangerous implications. Residency programs have decreased the amount of time spent in the neonatal intensive-care unit over a three-year program to three or four months. Therefore the residents and neonatal fellows are less experienced, and the clinical obligations of the attending physicians have increased. Many pediatric residents complete their training programs with very little hands-on experience in resuscitation and critical care and do everything they can post residency to avoid both the hospital in general and the neonatal intensive-care unit in particular. Does this approach offer the best care to our patients?

I read in national newspapers daily about cuts in health-care costs and different groups suing health-care organizations, alleging breach of contracts, deceptive business practices, and other mundane complaints. It is true that the *practice* of medicine today has become the *business* of medicine. Is it ever going to stop?

There may be an answer. There may be a new approach. Pediatric intensive-care specialists and neonatologists in California have organized and become proactive. Realizing that California has a very high percentage of managed care, a very low remuneration scale, and rapidly depleting physician and nursing resources, they organized a group called the California Coalition of Pediatric Subspecialists. They hired a lobbying and public relations firm and outlined a political agenda. They wrote letters and made telephone calls to key members of the Senate and Assembly Health Budget Committees. In addition, they requested a proposal to increase pediatric subspecialty remuneration to 100 percent of Medicare levels. Both Houses unanimously approved the request, although it was scaled down in the revised governor's budget. The group is now actively lobbying the governor to preserve this budget increase, citing less access to care, difficulty in retaining physicians in the state, and problems in recruitment. If we are successful in this approach, this process may serve as a catalyst for pediatric subspecialists in other states to organize in a similar fashion.

As physicians, we have never stood together as a group, for there were always others who would work for less. The line between quality of care and cost containment became fuzzy. The American Academy of Pediatrics has recognized this dilemma and several national committees are considering these issues. Many doctors have felt that socialized medicine should be avoided at all costs, but perhaps both health professionals and patients would be better off. The Health Care Financing Administration and the American Medical Association have done their best but a new cottage industry of coding and documentation is now flourishing.

I no longer see younger colleagues with the same futuristic goals. Where will the leaders come from? Hospitals are failing; physician groups are going bankrupt; there have been further cuts in health-care financing—who would feel optimistic?

As in "Ring around the Rosy," we are falling down. This trickle needs to stop. Sooner or later it will affect all of us who are practicing neonatology. Budget cuts and more onerous requirements will mean longer hours, less remuneration, and dissatisfaction with our lives.

A Timely Scenario

Neonatologists sat on a wall.
Neonatologists had a great fall.
All the king's horses,
and all the king's men,
couldn't put our profession together again.

Future Financial Neonatal Shock
(Originally written in 1996 and updated in 2004, 2008, and 2013)

The predictions have all come full circle.

I have been a neonatologist for twenty years or so,
and have always felt secure about the things I really know.
At 600 grams with RDS, I could write a thesis,
on PFC or PDA and even gastroschisis.

I spend the time, put in the hours, sometimes without sleep,
a multidisciplinary-team approach, the company I keep.
The challenge remains; ideals still high, sometimes sad or funny,
but somehow through this experience, I need to earn some money.

As I grew up, I placed a charge and never did feel nervous,
a UAC, an ET tube, simply "Fee for Service."
Standby section, H&P, bill without confusion,
figure out a market price for exchange transfusion.

Then the task grew difficult; I can tell the tale,
in 1970 came along, the "Relative Value Scale."
The AMA devised a term which enlarged all my nodes,
you are all familiar with CPT word codes.

A Timely Scenario

99431 or two—, do these numbers jive?
Do I charge for standby? When did I arrive?
Was my original consultation limited or not?
Is 99252 the code? Tell me what I've got.

The charge sheets are so complicated and bring out all my wrath,
a simple task in '75 now takes a billing staff.
Bills are sent and evaluated, with the proper guide,
we wait and wait and wait and wait…finally it's denied.

Signed up too late, not eligible…tell me what to feel,
it's OK, Doc, perhaps you'll win on the third or fourth appeal.
I charge this, and you pay that—who decides the rules?
In the scheme of bill and pay, the docs appear as fools.

Discounted fees, per diem, bundling, RBRVS,
Current Procedural Terminology—it really is a mess.
Then IPAs and HMOs came upon the scene,
further discounts—what to do? They make us lean and mean.

Lesser payments, more paperwork, should I cry or laugh?
I hired a practice consultant and increased my billing staff.
Overhead goes up, employees too; life's become a wreck—
working harder, with much less fun and a dwindling check.

A new word crops up; we will be saved, with great anticipation.
Take weekend courses, learn the lingo known as "capitation."
How many lives are in your group? I need the enrollment disk,
length of stay turns my hair gray, for now I am at risk.

The future doesn't seem too bright. What happened to the fees?
Soon neonatal care will develop many DRGs.
"At risk for one, and one for all," will be our battle cry,
bill correctly, with proper codes; promise you will try.

Place the statement in the envelope; post it, do not fail,
hope that when you follow up you won't get a "voice mail".
Try and try and try again; this isn't "Poppycock".
A better term is **Future Financial Neonatal Shock**."

Future Financial Neonatal Shock—Postscript, 2004

Since 1996, my friends, we've mastered some new tricks,
the end result, however, still leaves us in a fix.
We devised the global code, used but once each day,
removed procedures—no more bundling—to make things less gray.

Is the "critical patient" well defined? To be or not to be?
When does 99296 become 99233?
And then the weight-specific IC codes came upon the scene,
a gram or two, a new RVU—many thought this keen.

Now we deal with days of age, I need to hide and run,
is twenty-eight the proper number, or is it thirty-one?
We are told to use a pediatric code, after XX days,
a cloud appears on the horizon; it all seems such a haze.

Interpret black; interpret white, auditors don't quibble.
Why, we ask, are some evals stuck right in the middle?
New addendums added yearly make my eyelids droop,
now we need to qualify if we work in one specific group.

When NNPs joined the team, it really felt terrific,
and now we note that billing rules are often state specific.
Federal and state control—a preying velociraptor,
in the end they will devise a new "conversion factor."

So, colleagues, we're all profiled and probably underrated,
do not let coding rules leave you constipated.
Try and try again, you all; this isn't **"Poppycock"**,
a better term is **"Future Financial Neonatal Shock."**

Future Financial Neonatal Shock—Postscript, 2008

Since 2004, my friends, we sit around and mope,
with all the changes we endure, it's sometimes hard to cope.
The global weight-based codes were formulated to make our coding easy,
but insurance companies have resisted; this situation makes me queasy.

"Send me the baby's chart"—a request that makes me flinch,
they believe that three month's care will record to an inch.
Handwritten notes are hard to read, you can win the prize,
if you convert to modern times and computerize.

Then publications are released, with addended rules,
Maalox, Mylanta, Kaopectate won't help my frequent stools.
CPT Assistant, Coding Alert for Pediatrics—offered with a tease,
pay the exorbitant subscription; it will make you wheeze.

And then the Federal Government, on behalf of CMS,
complicated matters, adding to our distress.
Are the RVUs they quote truly real or not?
Use the modification factor...tell me what I've got.

A new code for 2008—99477—
was supposed to take all neo coders on the way to heaven.
A new question immediately arises on the spot,
"is this baby really intensive, or is this baby not?"

You say "tomato," and I say "tomahto,"
you say "potato," and I say "potahto."
Potato, potahto..... Tomato, tomahto,
this whole topic is too, too hot.

In 2009 we will renumber all the codes,
the highways, byways, and freeways will tangle up our roads.
Try and try again; this isn't **"Poppycock".**
a better term is **"Future Financial Neonatal Shock."**

Future Financial Neonatal Shock—Postscript, 2013

Since 2008, my friends, our practices are rated.
Seeing patients, placing codes became more complicated.
Critical, intensive—what is this sensation?
How can we determine imminent deterioration?

Patient names now are blocked, this is not too cool,
but we are told that we must follow every HIPPA rule.
Monikers—no longer "Doc" or "Nurse"—seem to be congressional,
CPT has coined the term "Qualified Health-Care Professional."

Take the courses, read the books, renumber every code,
a neo section in CPT—it is a winding road.
The date of birth, now day zero, isn't any fun,
for forty years or so, I've counted it as "one."

Transport supervision in the past seemed so very easy,
newer guidelines and restrictions really make me queasy.
A new procedure in the last few years, head or body cooling,
is difficult to code at best and has led to increased stooling.

Moderate sedation, so detailed, how much did you do?
Chills run up and down my spine—is this just fear or flu?
And then consultation codes deleted, left me in a pickle,
all my time and expertise are not worth one damn nickel!

A Timely Scenario

New modes of ventilation, antibiotics with longer names,
now recertification—why play these silly games?
Progression from HFV to IMV...a gap,
High-Flow Nasal Cannula—is this in fact CPAP?

Great debates for many years, the company we keep,
supine or side positioning—or is it back to sleep?
Now music in the incubator soothes the preemie soul,
Beethoven or Streisand? Will the kid like rock 'n' roll?

Bring back "fee for service," a memory from the past,
when first instituted, we all felt it would last.
Quality improvement insists we evaluate the data,
DRGs are coming soon, it really doesn't "matta."

But, oh, my friends, there are new models; just you wait and see,
ACOs are in gestation, and so is P4P.
The ACA or Obamacare has spread throughout our nation,
we deal consistently with obfuscation and/or obumbration.

Read again the comments of '96, '04, '08,
so much hasn't really changed—what will be our fate?
ICD-9 and 10 and eventually 11,
add specificity and sensitivity to take us all to heaven.

Try and try again, again; this isn't **"Poppycock"**,
a better term is **"Future Financial Neonatal Shock."**

Finale

I hope you have enjoyed reading these essays, poems and commentaries. As with most medical issues, things are not always smooth and there are bumps in the road which are often externally instigated. However, I believe that we as a subspecialty are successfully maneuvering around these obstacles with a clear vision of the future.

A final thought:

IT IS BETTER TO CURSE THE DARKNESS THAN TO LIGHT THE WRONG CANDLE.

Gilbert I. Martin, M.D.